Funk & Wagnalls
Dictionary of Data Processing Terms

FUNK & WAGNALLS
DICTIONARY of
DATA
PROCESSING
TERMS

Harold A. Rodgers

FUNK & WAGNALLS / New York

Contents

Introduction
by Harold A. Rodgers

It is unlikely that any field has contributed more new terms (or new meanings of old ones) to the language in the last few years than has data processing. This is largely because data processing is itself a new concept. While any procedure that involves the organization or classification of data can be referred to as data processing, the term refers primarily to such procedures as are carried out automatically by machines, principally the digital computer.

This book attempts to cover the terms used in reference to hardware, programing, software, logic, and Boolean algebra, and also the terms used in ancillary fields, such as data communications. Included also are terms from areas of frequent application, in particular, mathematics. Those terms that refer to hardware from the engineering viewpoint, however, are by and large excluded; these terms are covered in Funk & Wagnalls *Dictionary of Electronics.*

The definitions themselves are reasonably simple, but not so simple as to compromise the usefulness of the book through the omission or distortion of important concepts. We have striven to provide maximum generality; in particular, we have not included terms or meanings which, to our knowledge, are specific to a particular manufacturer of data-processing equipment. Illustrations have been provided at points where they were felt to be useful or necessary.

While this book has been prepared with great care, it cannot and does not claim to be a final authority; language (and especially the language of data processing) is a constantly changing phenomenon. We offer this work in the spirit of assistance rather than that of prescription.

A

abort *v.* To terminate execution of (a program) when an irrecoverable error, mistake, or malfunction occurs.

absolute address **1** An address that is permanently assigned to a particular storage location within the machine. **2** A series of characters that with no further modification refers to a particular storage location.

absolute code CODE in which all addresses are absolute and all OPERATION CODES are in MACHINE LANGUAGE. — **absolute coding**

absolute error **1** The actual error contained in a quantity, expressed in the same units. **2** The ABSOLUTE VALUE of an error.

absolute value The actual magnitude of a quantity, disregarding its algebraic sign or, in the case of a vector, its direction.

absolute value sign A sign | | indicating that the absolute value of a number is to be taken, for example, $|\pm k| = k$.

abstract **1** *n.* A summary or epitome, as of a document. **2** *v.* To prepare an abstract of.

3 *adj.* Lacking any specific reference or indication of its meaning, as a symbol or character.

acceleration time In the processing of magnetic tape, the time that elapses between the interpretation of a READ or WRITE instruction and the possibility of information transfer between tape and internal storage.

access *n.* The placing of data in or retrieving of data from storage. See RANDOM ACCESS, REMOTE ACCESS, SERIAL ACCESS.

access arm In a DISC STORAGE unit, a part that holds and positions one or more reading and writing heads.

access method Any of the available techniques for transferring data between main storage and an input/output device.

access mode In COBOL, a technique used to fetch or load a particular logic record from or into a file that is assigned to a mass storage device.

access time **1** The time that elapses between the instant at which an item of data is called for from storage and the instant at which its delivery is completed; read time. **2** The time that elapses between the instant at which an item of data is requested to be stored and the instant at which its storage is completed; write time.

accumulator *n.* A REGISTER in which are formed sums (often of repeated additions) and results of other arithmetical and logical operations.

accuracy *n.* Correctness; in particular, the degree to which a given result is free from incorrect computations. Compare PRECISION.

accuracy control character A control character associated with a given block of data, designed to indicate if the data are in error, are to be disregarded, or cannot be represented on a particular device.

acoustic delay line A DELAY LINE whose operation depends on the speed with which sound propagates in some fluid.

acoustic storage A storage device whose principal operating elements are acoustic delay lines.

active network An electrical network that contains any sources of power other than signal inputs.

activity *n.* Any operation or new data that results in reference to or modification of the data stored in a FILE.

activity ratio In a data file, the ratio of the number of RECORDS showing activity to the number of records in the file.

addend *n.* An AUGEND.

adder *n.* A device that delivers an output that is equal to the sum of its inputs. See HALF-ADDER.

adder-subtractor A device that delivers an output or outputs equal to the sum or difference or both of its inputs.

addition *n.* In arithmetic, an operation equivalent to the determination of the MEASURE *c* of the set *C* that can be expressed as the UNION of the sets *A* of measure *a* and *B* of measure *b*, where the INTERSECTION of *A* and *B* is the NULL SET.

additive inverse That number *x* which when added to another number *a* produces a sum equal to the inentity element with respect to addition, that is to say, zero. By convention the additive inverse of *a* is notated — *a*.

address *n.* A set of characters that uniquely identifies a particular location or destination in a data system, as, for instance a location in storage or a station in a communications network.

address constant A BASE ADDRESS.

address format **1** In a machine instruction, the arrangement of the parts that specify addresses. **2** The arrangement of the parts in a single address, as for instance, the various levels of addressing required to locate an item in a disc system.

address part A part of an instruction that constitutes an address, either of an operand, instruction, or result.

add time The time required for the performance of an addition operation exclusive of the time spent transferring operands and results to and from storage.

adjacency *n.* In character recognition, a condition in which the spacing reference lines for a pair of consecutive characters printed on the same line are less than a specified distance apart.

ALGOL (ALGOrithmic Language) A procedure-oriented language designed to accommodate mathematical formulas.

algorithm *n.* A set of well-defined rules or procedures that can be used to solve a given problem in a finite number of steps.

alias *n.* Any of a set of labels that have the same referent; an alternate label.

alpha *adj.* Of or indicating alphabetic characteristics; alphabetic.

alphabet *n.* An ordered set composed of all the letters and special marks used in a language.

alphameric *adj.* Indicating or pertaining to a set of characters that contains numerals as well as letters and special marks.

alphanumeric *adj.* Alphameric.

alteration switch In a digital computer, a manually-operated, console-mounted switch which can be used to supply one bit of information to a program.

ambient noise Any undesired sounds existing in a particular location.

analog **1** *adj.* Indicating or pertaining to the representation of quantities in (ideally) continuously variable physical form, as, for example, in the form of a time-varying voltage or current. **2** *n.* A quantity that is an analog representation of another.

analog computer A computer in which representation and operations are carried out in analog form, that is, using continuously variable physical quantities.

AND *n.* A logical operator having the property that if $a_1, a_2, \ldots a_n$ are a set A of statements, the statement a_1 AND $a_2 \ldots$ AND a_n is true if and only if all of the members of A are true. In an equivalent alternate sense, if the set A is composed of variables having the possible values 0, 1, then $a_1 \cdot a_2 \cdot \ldots a_n = 1$ if and only if all of the members of the set A have the value 1.

Truth table for
AND operator

A	B	A·B*
0	0	0
0	1	0
1	0	0
1	1	1

* A · B is symbolic notation for A **AND** B

AND-gate A logic module, often an electronic circuit, having *n* inputs and the property that its output is 'on' only when all of its inputs are 'on.'

answering time In data communications, the time that elapses between the appearance of a signal and the response made to it.

arbitrary sequence computer A computer in which each instruction determines its successor.

area *n.* **1** A set of consecutively numbered locations in main storage. **2** A CLEAR AREA.

area search The examination of a large set of documents in order to find those which are members of some defined subset.

argument *n.* An independent variable, that is, a variable upon whose value the value of some function depends.

arithmetic mean See AVERAGE.

arithmetic operation Any of the operations used in arithmetic, principally addition, subtraction, multiplication, and division, but including also raising to powers, extraction of roots, negation, and absolute value.

arithmetic shift A shift that does not affect the sign bit, equivalent to a multiplication by R^n, where R is the radix of the number system used and n is a positive or negative integer.

arithmetic unit The part of a computing system that performs arithmetic operations.

array *n.* An arrangement of elements either in a sequence or in a grid of two or more dimensions. In a two-dimensional array, for example, each element is identified by its position in a column and its position in a row.

articulation *n.* In a communications channel, the percentage of spoken phonemes that can be correctly understood by a listener.

artificial intelligence The ability of a device or system to function as though, in effect, endowed with intelligence, as for example, by learning from past experience.

artificial language A language based on an arbitrary, but generally self-consistent, set of rules (a grammar, as it were) established prior to its use.

ASCII A(merican) S(tandard) C(ode for) I(nformation) I(nterchange) An eight-bit data-transfer code adopted by the American Standards Association.

assembler *n.* A computer program that implements assembly.

assembler language A symbolic language associated with a particular assembler.

assembly *n.* The translation of a source program written in a symbolic language into an object program in machine language.

assembly time The occasion on which a source language program is assembled.

associative storage A storage device in which locations are identified by their contents rather than by names or positions.

asynchronous *adj.* Unpredictable or irregular with respect to time of occurrence; not synchronized.

asynchronous computer A computer in which the initiation of any particular operation depends on a signal that the previous operation has been terminated. Compare SYNCHRONOUS COMPUTER.

asynchronous transmission Data transmission in which the synchronization for each information character is performed individually, generally by means of START PULSES and STOP PULSES.

atmospherics *n. pl.* Electrical noise originating in the atmosphere, as from lightning flashes; also, such noise as picked up by a radio receiving system.

attenuator *n.* A device designed to introduce signal loss into a transmission system, and often provide an improved impedance match as well.

audit **1** *n.* The operation used to check the correctness and validity of data introduced into a data-processing system. **2** *v.* The performance of an audit.

augend *n.* One of a pair of quantities which are to be added together, nominally the one to which the other is added.

auto-abstract **1** To select key words from a source document by means of data-processing. **2** A set of key words so prepared.

auto-index **1** To prepare an index to a corpus of material by means of data processing. **2** An index so prepared.

automatic calling unit A device supplied by a communications common carrier that permits automatic dialing of calls by a business machine.

automatic dialing unit A device that can automatically generate the digits necessary for dialing a call.

auxiliary equipment Equipment that is not directly or continuously controlled by the central processing unit of a computer.

auxiliary operation An operation performed by auxiliary equipment.

auxiliary storage Storage devices such as tape and disk which have inherently larger capacities than main storage but which have longer access times.

availability n. The ratio of available time to the total time.

available time The time during which a piece of equipment is available for use, that is, the time during which it is not under maintenance and is believed to be operating reliably.

average n. A number (A) that is a function of a set of numbers (x_i) and that is considered typical or representative of the set. In general

$$A(x_i) = (\sum_{i=1}^{n} q_i x_i^y / \sum_{i=1}^{n} q_i)^{1/y},$$

where q_i represents the weight given to each x_i, n is the number of x_i and y is arbitrary. If each of the q_i equals 1 and y equals 1 this average is called the arithmetic mean; if q_i are all 1 and y equals -1 this average is called the harmonic mean; with q_i again equal to 1 and y equal to 2 this average is called the root mean square. This formulation may be extended to cover any continuous function, $f(x)$, defined, together with its weighting function, $q(x)$, in the interval $a \leq x \leq b$. In this case

$$A[f(x)] = [\int_a^b q(x) f(x)^y \cdot dx / \int_a^b q(x)dx]^{1/y}.$$

See GEOMETRIC MEAN; MEAN.

B

babble n. Crosstalk or other interference from a number of other communications channels.

background noise The total noise in a communications system regardless of the presence or absence of a signal.

background processing The automatic reversion of a data-processing system to the execution of lower priority programs during intervals in which higher priority programs have relinquished system resources.

backspace v. To translate the reading or display position backwards as prescribed.

backspace character A control character that causes backspacing to be performed.

balanced adj. Indicating an electrical transmission line or network in which the impedances measured from corresponding points on opposite sides are equal with respect to ground.

band *n.* **1** A range of frequencies bounded by two specified limits. **2** On a drum, disk, or similar storage device, a group of circular recording tracks.

bandpass filter A wave filter that passes a particular band of frequencies with negligible attenuation while attenuating all others sharply.

bandwidth *n.* The difference in hertz (cycles per second) between the frequencies that define the limits of a band.

bank *n.* A set of similar devices, as relays, transformers, lamps, etc., connected together and used in conjunction.

base *n.* **1** A reference value, as used for example in computing addresses. **2** In a number system, the number of possible digits that can be used in one place in expressing an integer, more explicitly a positive number b such that any positive integer can be written in the form $d_0 + d_1b + d_2b^2 + \ldots + d_nb^n$, where each of the $d_0, d_1, \ldots d_n$ are nonnegative integers smaller than b.

base address A constant from which an absolute address is computed by combination with a relative address; an address constant.

base point A dot used to separate the fractional and integral parts of a number as written in positional notation, most often a decimal point or binary point.

basic access method An access method in which as a result of each input/output statement there occurs a particular machine input/output operation.

batch processing **1** A technique of running a set of programs so that they are executed in sequence; also, loosely the sequential execution of programs. **2** A technique in which a number of similar programs are grouped and processed during the same machine run.

baud *n.* The measure of telegraph signaling speed, defined as a rate of one pulse (of the shortest duration used in the system) per second.

Baudot code The standard five-bit teletypewriter code. In practice the five pulses (bits) representing any character are always preceded by a start pulse, which is always a spacing pulse (0), and are followed by a stop pulse, which is always a marking pulse (1).

bay *n.* A vertical rack or housing for electronic equipment.

B-box An INDEX REGISTER.

BCD *abbr.* BINARY CODED DECIMAL NOTATION.

bel 1 *abbr.* The BELL CHARACTER. **2** See DECIBEL.

bell character A control character that activates a signal that calls for human attention or intervention.

benchmark *n.* A point of reference chosen for making measurements and comparisons.

benchmark problem A problem that can be run on various computers in order to evaluate and compare their performances.

bias *n.* **1** In statistics, the difference between the mean of the distribution of an ESTIMATOR and the parameter that it estimates. **2** A steady-state force, voltage, magnetic field, etc., applied to a system or device to establish a reference level or determine the range of operation.

bias distortion In teletypewriter applicat*i*ons, the uniform displacement of the leading edges of the MARK pulses from their correct positions with respect to the leading edge of the START PULSE.

bid *n.* An attempt to seize and send traffic over a communications line that is dedicated.

bidirectional flow In flowcharting, a flow that can traverse the same flowline in either direction.

binary *adj.* **1** Indicating a condition, selection, etc., in which there is a restriction to two and only two possibilities. **2** Indicating a number system in which 2 (notated as 10 in the system) is used as the base or radix.

binary card A card on which data has been represented in COLUMN BINARY or ROW BINARY form.

binary cell A storage device capable of holding a single binary digit.

binary code A code that uses two and only two distinct elements. See also GRAY CODE.

binary coded decimal notation A form of numerical notation in which the individual digits that make up a decimal number are written as binary numbers. The decimal 128, for example, would be written, 0001 0010 1000 in binary coded decimal form as contrasted with 10000000 in straight binary form.

binary counter A counting device, most often an electronic circuit, having two and only two distinct states per stage, each stage flipping from one state to the other when triggered.

binary digit **1** Either of the characters 0 or 1, or either of another equivalent pair. **2** A BIT.

binary incremental representation A form of incremental notation in which each increment is quantized so as to be representable as ± 1.

binary notation A form of positional notation in which the base or radix is 2. The system is analogous to decimal notation, the value of each place being 2^n, where n is an integer associated with each place in such a way that the place to the left of the point (explicit or implied) is associated with $n = 0$, n undergoing unit increments or decrements with successive places to the left or right, respectively. Thus 4.75 (decimal) is written as 100.11 (binary).

binary number **1** A number expressed in BINARY NOTATION. **2** Loosely, a BINARY NUMERAL.

binary numeral A binary number used to represent one of the digits of a decimal number, as in BINARY CODED DECIMAL NOTATION.

binary search A search technique in which a corpus is divided into two parts and the part that does not contain the desired item is rejected, the process being iterated until the desired item is isolated.

binary unit A BINARY DIGIT; a BIT.

bionics *n.* The study of animals as "living systems" for the purpose of modeling electronic and other technological systems after them.

bipolar *adj.* Polar.

biquinary code A method of representing decimal digits as a sum of two digits, the leftmost being 0 or 1 with a significance of 5, the other being 0, 1, 2, 3, or 4 with unit significance.

bistable *adj.* Indicating a device having two and only two states in which it is stable.

bit *n.* **1** A BINARY DIGIT. **2** In information theory, a measure of information equal to that given by a decision between two equiprobable alternatives. More generally, if there are n equiprobable alternatives the information H is given by $H = \log_2 n$. More generally still, if the choices are not equiprobable, $H = \sum_{i=1}^{n} -p_i \log_2 p_i$, where p_i is the probability associated with each individual n_i.

bit bucket In programmer slang, a hypothetical location, actually nonexistent, in which the bits lost during shifting operations are considered to accumulate.

bit density The number of bits stored per unit length, per unit area, or per unit volume, as specified.

bit location A position in a storage medium in which one bit can be stored.

bit rate The rate, with respect to time, at which bits are transmitted.

bit stream A transmitted series of binary digits considered without regard to grouping.

bit string A series of binary digits considered without regard to grouping.

black box A device or module whose contents are unknown or unspecified but whose inputs and outputs are related by a known set of rules.

blank *n.* **1** A part of a storage medium in which there are no characters recorded. **2** A code character indicating that no information is present.

blank character A SPACE CHARACTER.

blank coil Tape, as used for perforation, punched only with feed holes.

blank deleter A device which prevents the reception of blanks punched in paper tape.

blast **1** *n.* The release of a specified storage area or areas no longer needed by an operational program. **2** *v.* To release or cause the release of one or more specified storage areas.

blind *v.* To cause (a receiving device) to reject unwanted data by use of field definition characters.

block **1** *n.* A set of words, characters, digits, records, etc., that is in some way processed or handled as a unit. **2** *v.* To combine (two or more records) into a block.

block cancel character A character that causes the portion of a block preceding it to be disregarded.

block diagram **1** A chart that indicates the sequence of major operations that a system must perform to handle a particular operation. **2** A diagram indicating the relationships and interconnections between circuits or other pieces of hardware. Compare FLOW-CHART.

block gap An INTERBLOCK GAP.

block ignore character A BLOCK CANCEL CHARACTER.

blocking factor On a tape, the number of RECORDS which are combined to form a single BLOCK.

block loading A type of FETCH that places the control section of a LOAD MODULE in contiguous positions in main storage.

block sort A sorting operation in which an entire FILE is separated on the highest-order portion of the KEY. It is usually implied that these segments are ordered separately and then placed adjacent to the entire file.

block transfer The transmission of one or more BLOCKS.

book message A message to be transmitted to two or more places.

Boolean *adj.* Of or relating to the English mathematician and logician George Boole (1815–64) or, more especially, to BOOLEAN ALGEBRA.

Boolean algebra A branch of mathematics first systematically developed by George Boole in about 1850. While it has applications in the theory of sets, the theory of relations, and the theory of probability, its principal application at present is very likely the study of logical connectives or operators. This makes it a valuable tool in the design and application of digital computers.

Boolean operator An operator used in Boolean algebra, especially (for data processing purposes) one used when this algebra is applied to logic. In this application the result of any operation is restricted to one of two values generally represented as 0 and 1. See DYADIC BOOLEAN OPERATOR; MONADIC BOOLEAN OPERATOR.

bootstrap *n.* A technique or configuration by which or in which a device can be made to bring itself into a desired condition by its own action, an example being the practice of beginning a machine routine with a set of instructions that will cause the rest of it to be loaded from an input device.

border-punched card A MARGIN-PUNCHED CARD.

borrow 1 *n.* In arithmetic, the operation inverse to a CARRY. **2** *v.* To perform this operation.

boundary *n.* A CHARACTER BOUNDARY.

box *n.* An INDEX REGISTER; a B-box.

bps *abbr.* Bits per second.

branch 1 *n.* A sequence of instructions included between two decision instructions. **2** *v.* To choose one of two or more such sequences. **3** *n.* A path that directly joins two NODES of a NETWORK or graph. **4** *n.* Loosely, a CONDITIONAL JUMP.

branch cable A cable that is part of a larger cable from which it departs to reach some particular point.

branchpoint *n.* A point in a routine at which one or another branch is selected.

breakpoint *n.* A point in a routine, identified by an instruction, by a digit contained in an instruction, or by some other means, where the routine can be interrupted and later restarted.

bridge tap An unterminated length of line connected across a transmission line somewhere between its ends.

broadband *adj.* For data communications purposes, indicating a channel whose bandwidth exceeds the 3–4 khz bandwidth necessary for high-grade voice communications.

broadcast *n.* A transmission sent to a number of destinations simultaneously.

BS *abbr.* BACKSPACE CHARACTER.

BTAM *abbr.* Basic Telecommunications Access Method.

bucket *n.* In general, any specific reference in storage.

buffer *n.* A device or system used to make two other devices or systems compatible, in particular, (1) a device or routine that compensates for differences in time of occurrence or rate of flow when data is transmitted between devices, or (2) a circuit put between two other circuits to prevent undesirable interaction.

bug *n.* **1** A fault or defect. **2** A semiautomatic telegraph transmitting key. It produces a series of dots when the lever is held in one position and a continuous dash when it is held in the other.

burst 1 *v.* To separate the sheets of (continuous-form paper). **2** *n.* In data transmission, a sequence of signals that is considered to be a single unit.

bus *n.* A conductor or system of conductors

that connects any of several sources to any of several destinations.

business machine Any of various types of equipment, generally customer-provided, that connects to the lines of a common carrier for purposes of data movement.

bussback *n.* Feedback provided between the output and input portions of a common carrier circuit.

bust this A phrase appended to a message to indicate that it is to be disregarded in its entirety.

byte *n.* A normally short sequence of adjacent bits that is treated as a unit.

C

cable *n.* One or more wires or transmission lines mechanically assembled into a compact form, often with a protective sheath.

calculator *n.* A device that carries out arithmetic operations automatically but requires frequent human intervention for purposes of entering new data and determining the sequence of operations.

calculus *n.* **1** The branch of mathematics that analyzes the behavior of FUNCTIONS by means of DERIVATIVES and INTEGRALS. **2** A set of rules and procedures for carrying out various logical or mathematical operations.

calculus of variations The theory dealing with the maxima and minima of definite integrals in which the integrand is a function of one to several independent variables and one to several dependent variables, and their derivatives.

call **1** *v.* To jump or transfer control to (a closed subroutine). **2** *v.* To initiate or attempt to initiate contact with (another communications station). **3** *n.* The use of a contact between two communications stations.

called party In a switched network, a party which without initiating it is involved in a call.

calling party In a switched network, the party that initiates a call.

calling sequence **1** The set of instructions and data needed to initialize and call a given subroutine. **2** The sequence in which a set of terminals sharing a common transmission line are interrogated.

call number A set of characters that identifies a subroutine and contains information about parameters to be inserted in it, or information to be used in generating it, or information about the operands.

camp-on A method by which a call is held for a line that is in use and an indication given when the line becomes free.

CAN *abbr.* The CANCEL CHARACTER.

cancel character A control character indicating that the data with which it is associated are erroneous or to be disregarded.

CANTRAN *abbr.* Can(cel) tran(smission).

capacitor storage A device that stores data in the form of electric charges held on capacitors.

card code On a punched card, the combinations of holes used to represent characters.

card column On a $3\frac{1}{4}'' \times 7\frac{3}{8}''$ punched card, a line of punching positions parallel to the short edge; more generally, any vertical line of punching positions on a card.

card deck A DECK.

card face The side of a punched card on which there is printing, or, if both sides are printed, the side of principal importance.

card feed A mechanism that inserts cards into a machine singly.

card field A fixed number of adjacent card columns reserved for data of some particular type.

card hopper A device in which cards are stacked in such a way that they are available to a card feed.

card image An accumulation of data that maps in a one-to-one relationship onto the contents of a punched card.

card punch A device that records information on cards by punching holes in appropriate positions.

card reader A device that senses the holes in punched cards and translates them into electrical pulses.

card row On a $3\frac{1}{4}'' \times 7\frac{3}{8}''$ punched card, a line of punching positions parallel to the long edge; more generally, any horizontal row of punching positions on a card.

card stacker An output device in which punched cards are collected.

card-to-tape Designating hardware that effects a direct transfer of information from punched cards to punched or magnetic tape.

CARR *abbr.* Carrier.

carriage control tape A tape containing the data that control line feed for a printing device.

carriage return An operation that returns a printing device to the first (leftmost) specified position without necessarily making a line advance.

carriage return character A control character that causes a carriage return to be performed.

carrier *n.* **1** A flow of energy, especially electrical or electromagnetic energy, that can be varied (modulated) in such a way as to cause it to carry information. **2** A COMMUNICATIONS COMMON CARRIER.

carrier system A method of dividing a single communications channel into a number of subchannels by modulating the subchannels onto a series of different carrier frequencies which in turn modulate the main carrier or are otherwise mixed. The individual carriers and their SIDEBANDS are separated at the receiving station by BANDPASS FILTERS and subsequently demodulated.

carry **1** *n.* A digit generated when an arithmetic operation generates in one column a quantity exceeding the radix of the number system. **2** *v.* To forward (such a digit) to another column, generally the next higher in order, for processing. **3** *n.* The performance of the operation of carrying. **4** *n.* An inverse carry; a borrow.

cascade **1** *v.* To arrange (two or more similar units or processes) so that they operate or occur serially. **2** *adj.* Indicating a set of cascaded units or processes.

cascaded carry In parallel addition, a carry generated when two digits generate a partial sum and a carry digit which are in turn added, the process being iterated until no further carries are generated. Compare HIGH-SPEED CARRY.

catalog 1 *n.* A set of item descriptions compiled in order together with the information necessary to gain access to the items. 2 *n.* The set of all data set indices kept by data management. 3 *v.* To include in a catalog.

cataloged data set A data set that is included in an index or a hierarchy of indices.

cataloged procedure A set of job control statements included in a cataloged data set and retrievable by means of an execute (EXEC) statement.

cathode ray storage A form of electrostatic storage in which an electron beam is used to sense the data.

cathode-ray tube An electron tube in which a beam of electrons is made to impinge on various parts of a phosphor-coated screen and form a visual display.

cathode-ray tube display A readout of data by means of a cathode-ray tube.

CAX *abbr.* COMMUNITY AUTOMATIC EXCHANGE.

CDC *abbr.* Call-directing code.

cell *n.* A BINARY CELL or STORAGE CELL.

center-feed tape Perforated tape in which the feed holes have their centers directly in line with the holes punched to represent data.

centerline *n.* A STROKE CENTERLINE.

central office The location in which a communications common carrier terminates customer lines and keeps the equipment necessary to interconnect those lines.

central processing unit The section of a computer that decodes and executes instructions.

central processor A central processing unit.

Centrex *n.* A central-office type telephone installation providing PABX service to a group of subscribers at one location, capable of providing direct inward dialing, direct distance dialing, etc.

chad *n.* The fragment of material removed to form a punch in a storage material, as tape or cards.

chadded *adj.* Indicating a punching operation performed on tape that results in the production of chad.

chadless *adj.* Indicating a punching operation performed on tape that results in the production of no chad.

chadless tape Perforated tape from which the chad does not fully separate, facilitating explanatory printing on the tape.

chad tape FULLY PERFORATED TAPE.

chain code The set or some subset of all possible *n*-bit words arranged in such a way that each successor is derivable from its neighbor by shifting one position to the left and dropping the high-order digit or by performing this operation and inserting a bit in the low-order position, provided that no word recurs until the cycle is complete. An example of such a set would be 000, 001, 010, 101, 011, 111, 110, 100, 000.

chained list An ordered data set containing not necessarily contiguous items from a larger or equal set, derived in such a way that each item contains the means for identifying its successor.

chaining A system of storing records in which each record is a part of a chained list.

chaining search A technique for retrieving data that is part of a chained list from a file.

chain printer A printer in which the type slugs are mounted on the links of a loop of chain that revolves rapidly.

change dump A DUMP that applies only to those storage locations whose contents have changed in some specified interval.

channel *n.* **1** Something that acts as a path for a signal. **2** A unit of peripheral hardware that controls one or more input/output devices. **3** The part of a data storage medium that can be reached by a given reading or writing station, as a TRACK or BAND.

channelize *v.* To divide (a communications circuit) into several channels.

CHAR. *abbr.* CHARACTER.

character *n.* A symbol, as a letter or digit, that is used in the representation of data or operations to be performed on data.

character boundary In character recognition, the largest rectangle that can be formed with one side at right angles to the document reference edge and each side tangent to the outline of a given character.

character check A check that verifies that the rules for the formation of characters have been observed.

character density The number of characters recorded per unit length or area.

character emitter A device that automatically emits a timed pulse or series of pulses representing one or more characters in some code.

characteristic *n.* **1** The integral part of a logarithm to the base ten. **2** The part of a floating-point number that represents its exponent. **3** A distinctive quality or property.

characteristic distortion DISTORTION that depends not only on the properties of a transmission system but also on the previous history of the system, as for example, distortion caused by reflected remnants of earlier signals.

characteristic impedance Of a transmission line, that impedance which when coupled to the output end line absorbs the transmitted energy without reflection. It depends on the electrical parameters of the line and the frequency of the transmitted signal.

characteristic overflow In floating-point arithmetic, a condition in which a positive exponent is generated that exceeds the storage or register capacity provided for it.

characteristic underflow A condition identical with characteristic overflow except that the exponent is negative.

character outline The pattern made by the stroke edges of a printed character.

character printer A device that prints characters one at a time.

character reader A device that translates characters printed on a document into a form suitable for machine processing.

character recognition The automatic identification, by machine, of written or printed characters, phonemes, or other such information.

character set A set of unique characters, especially one that is ordered.

character spacing reference line In character recognition, any of the vertical lines by means of which the horizontal spacing of characters is evaluated. Such a line either coincides with the centerline of a vertical stroke or bisects the horizontal sides of a CHARACTER BOUNDARY.

character string A string consisting of characters and only characters.

character subset A SUBSET of a CHARACTER SET, generally one whose members share some common feature.

chart [14] **closed subroutine**

chart *n.* A FLOWCHART.

check **1** *n.* A process used to determine or ensure accuracy. **2** *v.* To carry out or subject to such a process.

check bit (character, digit) A redundant bit (character, digit) included in data for checking purposes.

checkpoint *n.* A point in a routine where data is checked or recorded for restart purposes.

Chinese binary COLUMN BINARY.

chip *n.* **1** In microcircuitry, a thin slice of silicon cut from a larger wafer and treated so as to contain one or more semiconductor devices. **2** A CHAD.

CIOCS *abbr.* Communications Input/Output Control System.

circuit *n.* **1** An electrical network in which there exist one or more paths through which current can flow. **2** In communications, the means necessary to provide communication in both directions between two points.

circuit grade The information capacity of a circuit or channel, measured either in bandwidth or the rate of transmission. It follows from the SAMPLING THEOREM that these two measures are equivalent.

circuit load A LINE LOAD.

circuit noise level The noise level of a circuit, generally measured as a ratio, in decibels, to an arbitrarily chosen reference, or in adjusted decibels, a measurement weighted to represent the interfering effect under specified conditions.

circuit switching LINE SWITCHING.

circulating register A SHIFT REGISTER in which data are moved out of one end and into the other in an endless loop.

circulating storage A form of storage through which data move continuously in a closed loop.

CL *abbr.* CONTROL LEADER.

clamp-on CAMP-ON.

class *n.* A set whose elements have similar characteristics.

classify *v.* To arrange (data or information) in classes according to a system or rule.

clear *v.* To cause (a storage device) to take on a prescribed state, generally that which indicates zero or blank.

clear area In character recognition, an area specified to be kept free of printing or other marks not related to machine reading.

clear band A CLEAR AREA.

clock *n.* **1** A stable oscillator that produces a train of equispaced pulses used for synchronization. **2** A register or other device that counts such pulses to measure and indicate time.

clock pulse Any of the pulses produced by a CLOCK.

clock track A track containing a pattern of signals that provides a reference.

closed loop A loop (def. 1) whose execution will persist indefinitely unless some external intervention is made.

closed-loop control system A FEEDBACK CONTROL SYSTEM.

closed shop **1** Indicating a computer installation in which most of the programming is the responsibility of specialists rather than of the problem originators. **2** Indicating a computer installation in which the actual machine operation is carried on by full-time trained operators rather than by user-programmers.

closed subroutine A subroutine stored at one location and which can be linked to a main routine in as many places as necessary.

COAM equipment C(ustomer)-o(wned)-a(nd)-m(aintained) equipment connected to the lines of a communications common carrier.

COBOL A programming language designed for business applications. The name derives from Co(mmon) b(usiness)-o(riented) l(anguage).

code **1** *n.* A set of symbols and an unambiguous system of rules specifying how they may be used to represent information. **2** *v.* To represent information by means of a code; to encode.

code character A configuration of code elements used to represent a particular symbol.

code conversion The translation of information from one code into another.

code element Any of the primitive elements from which a code is constructed.

code extension character Any of various control characters that indicate that one or more of the code characters following it belongs to a code different from the one in use at the time.

code holes In perforated tape, the holes representing information, as distinguished from the feed or other holes.

code line A single coded instruction, usually occupying one line on a CODING SHEET.

coder *n.* A person whose principal function is to encode computer routines which he has not himself designed.

code set A complete and finite set of objects represented by a particular code.

code value Any of the elements included in a CODE SET.

coding scheme A CODE.

coding sheet A sheet of paper printed with a form on which a routine can be conveniently written in code.

collate *v.* To merge (two or more sets of items having mutually consistent ordering) into a single ordered set.

collating sequence An ordering assigned to a set of items in such a way that any pair of subsets that it contains is compatible with respect to collation.

collator *n.* A device that collates punched cards or other documents.

color *n.* In optical character recognition, the property of an image which depends on the reflective properties of an object that vary with the wavelength of incident light, the spectral composition of the incident light, and the response characteristics of the observer.

column *n.* Any vertical arrangement of characters, sets of characters, images, or the like.

column binary On punched cards, a form of data representation in which adjacent columns correspond to adjacent bits.

column split On punched cards, a form of data representation in which punched positions in the same column can be treated separately.

combination *n.* **1** An illegal code expression, indicating by its occurrence a mistake or malfunction. **2** Any subset of a set of objects without regard for order.

combination logic element A device having at least one output channel and which operates in such a way that each output channel takes on one of a number of discrete states as the function of the discrete states of the input channels if these exist.

COMLOGNET *abbr.* (Air Force) Com(bat) Log(istic) Net(work).

command *n.* **1** A signal that initiates a control function. **2** Loosely, a machine language instruction. **3** Loosely, an operator (def. 1).

command language A SOURCE LANGUAGE composed mainly of a set of operators, each of which invokes a particular function.

comment *n.* Any expression serving to identify or explain one or more steps in a routine while having no effect on the execution thereof.

comment code One or more code characters used to identify a COMMENT.

common area An area of storage which is shared by two or more routines.

common battery central office A central office that contains the power source which supplies transmitter and signal current for itself and its associated stations.

Common Business Oriented Language See COBOL.

common carrier A COMMUNICATIONS COMMON CARRIER.

common field A field to which two or more independent routines have access.

common language A machine sensible language that is shared by a group of computers and peripheral equipment.

common logarithm See LOGARITHM.

communication *n.* The faithful transfer of information between two or more points.

communication control character A character used to control some aspect of the transmission of data via communications networks.

communication data system A system, operating in real time, that acts to establish compatibility between a teletype station and a computer.

communication link The physical means by which communication is carried on.

communications channel Any means by which information can be transferred.

communications common carrier A company that sells communications services to the public and which is regulated by one or more government agencies.

community automatic exchange A small dial telephone office that serves a community.

commutative operation A DYADIC OPERATION in which the order of the operands is immaterial, that is the dyadic operator F is commutative if and only if $F(A, B) = F(B, A)$.

compandor *n.* A unit that combines the functions of a COMPRESSOR and an EXPANDOR.

comparator *n.* A device that compares two items of data.

compare *v.* To carry out a comparison.

comparison *n.* An operation in which two similar items of data are examined to determine their relationship with respect to magnitude, value, correspondence, or the like.

compilation time The occasion on which a source language is compiled.

compile *v.* To translate (a routine written in a source language or programming language) into a corresponding machine language routine.

compiler *n.* A routine that compiles a source language routine.

complement *n.* Either of two numbers which are derived by rule from a given number expressed to the base (radix) N and which are often useful in representing the negative of the given number. If the digits of the given number are $X_1, X_2, \ldots X_n$, the corresponding digits of the **radix-minus-one** $(N-1)$ **complement** are $(N-1) - X_1$, $(N-1) - X_2, \ldots (N-1) - X_n$. If 1 is added to the radix-minus-one complement, all carries being performed in the usual manner, the result is the **radix (N) complement.** If K' is the N complement of K, then $L + K' = L - K$, provided that in the addition carries out of the high-order position are dropped. A simple example should suffice. Consider 555 (radix 10); its $N - 1(9)$ complement is 444; its $N(10)$ complement is 445. Now, adding 555 and 445 we get 1000; dropping the high-order carry we get 000 or $555 - 555$. This method permits great simplification in the hardware of digital computers.

complementary operator In Boolean algebra, the operator NOT.

complete carry In parallel addition, an arrangement that allows all carries to propagate.

complex number Any number of the form $a + bi$, where a and b are real numbers and $i = \sqrt{-1}$.

component *n.* **1** Any basic part or element. **2** A SOLID STATE COMPONENT.

composited circuit A circuit which by means of FREQUENCY-DIVISION MULTIPLEXING can be used simultaneously for telephony and direct-current telegraphy.

compress *v.* To reduce some parameter of (a signal), as bandwidth, amplitude variation, duration, etc., while preserving its information content.

compressor *n.* A device that compresses a signal, in particular, an amplifier whose gain is automatically adjusted according to the signal level in such a way that weak signals are amplified more strongly than strong signals, the purpose being to reduce the range of signal strengths. Normally, in order to avoid creating distortion, a compresser acts relatively slowly.

compromise net An electrical network used with a HYBRID COIL to secure reasonable isolation between the two directions of transmission.

compromise network A compromise net.

computational stability The degree to which a computational process is insensitive to errors, mistakes, malfunctions, or the like.

computer *n.* A machine capable of accepting data and processing it by the application of mathematical and/or logical operations. See ANALOG COMPUTER, DIGITAL COMPUTER.

computer code A machine-language code used by a given computer.

computer instruction A machine-language instruction for a particular computer.

computer network A system composed of two or more interconnected computers.

computer program A set of instructions and/or statements designed to be used by a computer in accomplishing a desired result.

computer word A series of bits or characters that is treated as a unit and which, in particular, occupies a single storage location.

computing unit The part of a computer that performs arithmetic operations and logic operations and makes decisions; the central processor.

concatenated data set A set composed of data sets that are logically connected.

concave function The reflection of a CONVEX FUNCTION about its secant line.

concurrent *adj.* Indicating actions or events that take place within the same specified time interval. Compare SIMULTANEOUS.

condensing routine A routine that converts the format of a normal OBJECT PROGRAM, that is, a format in which each instruction takes a single card, into one in which one card holds several instructions.

condition *v.* To connect additional equipment to (a leased voice-grade channel) in order to bring its parameters to at least the minimum values required for data transmission.

conditional jump A jump that occurs if and only if a set of specified criteria are satisfied.

configuration *n.* The grouping and interconnection of the equipment that makes up a data-processing system.

congestion *n.* A condition in which the number of calls arriving at the various inputs of a communications network are too many for the network to handle at once and are subject to delay or loss. The concept applies in an analogous way to any system in which arriving "traffic" can exceed the number of "servers."

congestion theory A mathematical discipline that deals with the study of delays and losses that affect the traffic of items that move through a communication system.

conjugate *n.* Either of a pair of complex numbers that are related in such a way that their real parts are identical and the imaginary part of one is the negative of the imaginary part of the other.

connector *n.* A symbol that indicates the convergence or divergence of flowlines, used also to indicate that a flowline breaks and is continued elsewhere. See Table of Flowchart Symbols, p. 126.

consecutive *adj.* Indicating a pair of events which occur in sequence with no other such event intervening. Compare CONCURRENT; SEQUENTIAL; SIMULTANEOUS.

console *n.* The array of controls that allows an operator or maintenance engineer to communicate with and manually introduce data into a computer.

constant *n.* **1** An item of data that has a fixed or invariable value. **2** An address constant; a BASE ADDRESS.

constant area A section of storage devoted to constants.

constant ratio code A code in which the ratio of the number of 1's to the number of 0's used in representing any character is fixed.

constraint *n.* An equation or inequality that states restrictions on the variables of a system. For example, in a system containing mass (M) as one of its variables, the constraint $M \geq 0$ is usual.

constraint matrix In linear programming, the matrix formed by the coefficient columns and constant columns of the constraint equations.

content-addressed storage ASSOCIATIVE STORAGE.

contention *n.* **1** On a multidrop communication line, a condition in which two or more locations try to transmit at once. **2** A condition in which a number of users make unregulated attempts to seize control of a communications line.

contrast *n.* In optical character recognition, the differences in HUE, SATURATION, and brightness between the printed characters and the background.

control block A storage area through which various parts of the operating system communicate a particular type of control data.

control card A punched card that contains input data or parameters which initialize or modify a program.

control character A character whose occurrence starts or affects a CONTROL OPERATION in some way.

control circuits The electronic circuits that make up the CONTROL UNIT.

control computer A computer that, by means of inputs from appropriately connected sensor units and outputs connected to control devices, supervises and controls a process occurring in real time.

control data Data used to identify, select, execute, or modify another routine, record, file, operation, data value, or the like.

control function A CONTROL OPERATION.

control mode A state such that when all the terminals on a particular communication line are in that state the characters on the line are interpreted as CONTROL CHARACTERS performing LINE DISCIPLINE.

control operation An action such as the initiation or termination of a particular process. By convention, operations such as carriage return, rewind, end of transmission, etc., are included in this class, while data reading and transmission are not.

control panel 1 The manually operated part of a computer CONSOLE. 2 A PLUGBOARD.

control program Any of various programs that carry on input/output operations, error detection and recovery, program loading, communication with the operator, and the like.

control section A portion of a routine which the programmer designs and specifies to be an entity, all elements of which are to be loaded into contiguous locations of main storage. Thus, a control section is the smallest segment of a program that can be separately relocated.

control switching point Any of the regional, sectional, and primary centers necessary for nationwide dialing.

control total A sum formed by the addition of a designated field from each of a group of records, used for checking purposes.

control unit The part of a digital computer that FETCHES the instructions in proper sequence, decodes them, and issues the necessary control signals to the arithmetic unit and other modules.

control volume A VOLUME containing one or more of the indices of a CATALOG.

conversational mode A form of communication between a terminal and a computer in which each transmission by one elicits a response from the other.

convert *v.* 1 To change from one method or system of data processing to another. 2 To change (data) from one form of representation to another. — **conversion** *n.*

converter *n.* A device designed to change information from one form into another, as from analog to digital, parallel to serial, etc.

convex function A function $y = f(x)$ defined in the interval $a < x < b$, and having the property that for each individual x_i where $a < x_1 < x_i < x_2 < b$, $f(x_i) \leq L(x_i)$, where $L(x)$ is the linear function that coincides with $f(x)$ at x_1, x_2.

convex programming A special case of NONLINEAR PROGRAMMING in which the function to be optimized and the constraints are CONCAVE FUNCTIONS or CONVEX FUNCTIONS.

coordinate indexing An indexing system in which each of the descriptors associated with a particular is of equal rank, the document being identified by a unique combination of such descriptors

copy *v.* To create a representation of (source data) in a new location and possibly in another form while leaving the source data unchanged. Compare DUPLICATE.

core *n.* A MAGNETIC CORE.

core storage In a digital computer, a form of high-speed storage composed of an array of magnetic cores each of which can be magnetized in either of two polarities and which, therefore, are each able to store one BIT.

corner cut On a card, a corner cut off at an oblique angle to facilitate orientation.

corpus *n.* A mass of data, often in unreduced form, chosen for study.

corrective maintenance Maintenance designed to correct an existing fault condition.

corrective maintenance time The time occupied, generally on an unscheduled basis, by corrective maintenance.

cos *abbr.* Cosine.

cosecant *n.* See TRIGONOMETRIC FUNCTIONS.

cosine *n.* See TRIGONOMETRIC FUNCTIONS.

cotangent *n.* See TRIGONOMETRIC FUNCTIONS.'

counter *n.* **1** A device that switches to the next of *n* discrete states upon the receipt of each input pulse. A counter may be used in conjunction with a READOUT device that indicates which state it is in, or it may be set to deliver an output when it reaches a particular state. **2** An instruction counter.

cps *abbr.* **1** Characters per second. **2** Cycles per second. See also HERTZ.

CPU *abbr.* CENTRAL PROCESSING UNIT.

CR *abbr.* The CARRIAGE RETURN CHARACTER.

crossbar switch A special type of relay that can make a connection between any line chosen from one set and any line chosen from another set.

crossbar system A line-switching system that uses crossbar switches.

crossfire *n.* CROSSTALK between telegraph channels.

crosstalk Any undesired transfer of signals between two or more different communications channels.

CRT *abbr.* Cathode ray tube.

cryogenic *adj.* Of or having to do with temperatures approaching absolute zero.

cryogenics *n.* The branch of physics dealing with temperatures that approach absolute zero.

cryotron *n.* A device in which the magnetic field caused by the input current controls the superconducting-to-normal transition of the output circuit. A principal advantage of the cryotron is that it dissipates energy only while actually changing states.

crypto or **cryptographic** *adj.* Indicating equipment that transforms data into forms such that its actual meaning is not apparent, as by secret code conversion.

csc *abbr.* Cosecant.

CSP *abbr.* CONTROL SWITCHING POINT.

ctn *abbr.* Cotangent.

cue *n.* A CALL.

curtate *n.* On a card, a set of adjacent punched rows.

customer station equipment Equipment owned by a communications common carrier, used in conjunction with private line services, and located on the customer's premises.

cutoff *n.* The point at which attenuation and distortion render a signal unusable.

cybernetics *n.* The science that is concerned with the principles of communication and control, particularly as applied to the operation of machines and the functioning of organisms.

cycle *n.* **1** A series of sequential changes

occurring in a material system in such a way that the system is periodically restored to its initial condition and so that all the sets of changes are equivalent, in particular, the passage of a wave from its equilibrium position to its peak, then to its trough, and back to equilibrium. **2** A set of operations that is regularly repeated without variation in sequence but with possible variation in the details of each operation.

cycle index **1** The number of executions a cycle has undergone. **2** The difference (or its negative) between the desired number of executions of a cycle and the number actually performed.

cycle reset The setting of a cycle index to its initial or some other condition.

cycle time The time that elapses between the call for information from a storage device and the delivery of the information.

cyclic code A BINARY CODE in which the combinations representing two successive numbers differ by only one BIT.

cyclic redundancy check character In a modified cyclic code, a redundant character introduced for error detection purposes.

cyclic shift A shift operation in which the data moved out of one end of the register are reintroduced at the other end.

cyclic storage CIRCULATING STORAGE.

D

damping *n.* A characteristic designed into potentially oscillatory electrical or mechanical systems to prevent or eliminate undesired oscillation.

DASD *abbr.* Direct access storage device.

data *n.* Any set of objects, values, quantities, characters, or the like that represents INFORMATION.

data bank An extensive and comprehensive set of libraries of data.

data base A DATA BANK.

data code A set of characters structured in such a way as to represent the data items of a data element; for example the numbers 01–12 might represent, in order, the months of the year.

data collection The transmission, by whatever means, of data from one or more points to a central point.

data communication The transmission of data between points, generally by means of telecommunications systems.

data control block A control block through which access routines receive the information necessary to store and fetch data.

data conversion The changing of data from one manner of representation to another.

data element A class or category of data based on intrinsic or assigned relations between DATA ITEMS; for instance the data element "month" contains the data item "January."

data flowchart A FLOWCHART that indicates the flow of data through a problem solution.

data flow diagram A DATA FLOWCHART.

data gathering DATA COLLECTION.

data hierarchy A data arrangement composed of sets and subsets and having the property that every subset of any set is of lower order than the data of the set.

data item Any individual member of a DATA ELEMENT.

data link The communications lines and associated hardware used in transmitting data between two or more points.

data link escape character In data communication, a control character that in conjunction with one or more succeeding characters forms an escape sequence, providing by some means additional data communication control operations.

data logging The recording of data concerning events that occur sequentially in time.

data loop transceiver The STATION ARRANGEMENT or DATA SET for Class D leased data channels provided by Western Union.

data management All those functions of a control program that provide access to data sets, enforce data storage conventions, and regulate the use of input/output devices.

data medium 1 Any material medium in which or on which, by variation in one or more of its physical parameters, data can be represented. 2 The physical parameter thus varied.

data name A symbol that specifies a unique item of data.

data organization In data management, any of the conventions for the arrangement of a data set.

data origination The representation of source information in machine-readable or electrical form.

Data-Phone 1 The transmission of data by means of the telephone network: a service mark of American Telephone & Telegraph and the Bell System. 2 The equipment supplied by the carrier in order to accomplish this: a trademark of American Telephone & Telegraph and the Bell System.

data processing The performance of a systematic set of operations upon data.

data-processing system A set of interconnected machine components capable of performing data processing.

data processor Any device, whether automatic or not, that is capable of any form of data processing.

data purification In general, the removal of as many erroneous or spurious items as possible from a mass of data prior to the application of automatic data processing.

data reduction Any of the operations performed on raw data to make it more readily useful, as, for instance, the weighting of a set of experimental results.

data set 1 A collection of data in a prescribed format described by control information to which an operating system has access, constituting the principal unit of data storage and retrieval within the system. 2 A device that provides compatibility between business machines and communications services.

data set clocking In a data set (def. 2), an oscillator that generates a time base used to regulate the rate at which bits are transmitted. * This is often called *external clocking* by computer manufacturers and *internal clocking* by communications common carriers.

data set control block A DATA SET LABEL attached to a data set in direct access storage.

data set label Information that describes the attributes of a data set and which is normally stored with it.

data signaling rate The capacity, in bits per second, of a set of parallel communications channels.

data sink In communications, a device that is able to accept data signals, in some cases checking them and generating error control signals.

data source In communications, a device that is able to originate data signals for transmission, and, in some cases, receive and respond to error control signals.

DATASPEED A marketing term used by American Telephone & Telegraph for a line of medium-speed paper tape transmitting and receiving units. See also TELESPEED.

data terminal equipment A DATA SOURCE, a DATA SINK, or a combination of both.

data transmission The transfer of data between parts of a system.

data use identifier A name, title, or description that specifies the intended use of a DATA ELEMENT.

db or **dB** abbr. DECIBEL(S).

dbm abbr. DECIBEL(S) referred to one milliwatt.

DC1, DC2, DC3, ... etc. DEVICE CONTROL CHARACTERS.

DDA abbr. DIGITAL DIFFERENTIAL ANALYZER.

DDD abbr. DIRECT DISTANCE DIALING.

dead band In a control system, an interval through which the controlled variable can vary without initiating any effective system response.

dead time The time interval after the arrival of a pulse, during which a COUNTER is insensitive to the arrival of a second pulse.

debug v. **1** To free a piece of apparatus of malfunctions, especially as one of the stages in its design. **2** To locate and correct the mistakes in a computer program.

decade n. The interval between the limits $k \times 10^n$ and $k \times 10^{n+1}$, as, for example, the interval between 30 and 300 or between 100 and 1,000.

deceleration time The time required to stop a tape after the last item in a record on that tape has been read.

decibel n. A unit used to express ratios of signal power, defined in such a way that n, the number of decibels, is given by

$$n = 10 \log_{10} P_2/P_1,$$

where $P_{1,2}$ are the power levels. It follows that if $L_{1,2}$ are levels of current, voltage, or quantities that are their analogs, then

$$n = 20 \log_{10} L_2/L_1.$$

Since decibels represent a ratio it is necessary to establish a reference for 0 decibels in order to indicate an absolute level.

decimal adj. **1** Indicating a property that involves a choice in which there are ten possibilities. **2** Of or having to do with the system of numeration that uses 10 as its radix.

decimal digit In decimal notation, any of the characters 1, 2, 3, 4, 5, 6, 7, 8, 9, 0.

decimal notation A FIXED RADIX NOTATION based on ten.

decimal numeral The set of characters that represents, in decimal notation, some particular number.

decimal point In decimal notation, the RADIX POINT.

decision *n.* A choice between two or more possibilities, in particular, a choice between two or more future courses of action in a routine.

decision instruction An instruction that causes a computer to follow one of two or more BRANCHES of a routine.

decision table A table that enumerates all the contingencies that can arise in the description of a problem, and the action to be taken in each particular case.

deck *n.* A set of punched cards.

decode *v.* To apply a code to (encoded data) in such a way as to perform the inverse of the previous encoding.

decoder *n.* **1** One who or that which decodes. **2** A MATRIX (def. 2). **3** An OPERATION DECODER.

decollate *v.* To divide (a multipart form or paper stock) into separate piles.

decrement **1** *n.* A negative INCREMENT. **2** *n.* In certain computers, a particular part of an instruction word. **3** *v.* To apply a negative increment to.

dedicated service A leased facility or a private line.

deferred entry A subroutine entry that occurs as a result of a DEFERRED EXIT.

deferred exit The transfer of control to a subroutine in such a way that the time of transfer is determined by an asynchronous rather than a predictable event.

DEL *abbr.* The DELETE CHARACTER.

delay *n.* The amount of time by which an effect is retarded with respect to its cause.

delay distortion A form of distortion that arises when the rate of signal transmission through a line or transducer varies as a function of frequency within the bandwidth required for transmission.

delay equalizer An electrical network designed to compensate for DELAY DISTORTION.

delay line A device connected between two points in order to cause a signal that arrives at the first point to reach the second with a predetermined time delay.

deleave *v.* To DECOLLATE.

delete character A character whose primary use is the obliteration of erroneous or undesired characters.

deletion record A record that will serve to replace or remove an existing record contained in a master file.

delimiter *n.* A FLAG that serves to separate and organize various items of data.

delta function The generalized function

$$\delta(t - t_0),$$

defined in such a way that

$$\int g(t)\,\delta(t - t_0) = g(t_0),$$

provided that t_0 is in the range of integration. One of its important properties is that

$$\int_{-x}^{t} \delta(t) = u(t),$$

where $u(t)$ is a unit STEP FUNCTION at $t - 0$.

demarcation strip Generally a terminal board that forms the interface between a business machine and common carrier equipment.

demodulate *v.* To recover from (a modulated wave) the information imparted by modulation. **— demodulator** *n.* **— demodulation** *n.*

denominator *n.* In a fraction, the number by which the other number is understood to be divided.

density *n.* RECORDING DENSITY.

derivative *n.* The instantaneous rate of change of a FUNCTION with respect to its independent variable, that is, given a function f(x), its derivative f'(x) is defined by

$$f'(x) = \lim_{h \to 0} [f(x + h) - f(x)]/h,$$

provided that this limit exists. Alternative notations for the derivative exist, so that

$$f'(x) = dy/dx = D_x, \text{ and if } y = f(x), y' = f'(x).$$

See PARTIAL DERIVATIVE.

description *n.* A PROBLEM DESCRIPTION.

descriptor *n.* A WORD that serves to categorize or index information for retrieval.

design *n.* **1** FUNCTIONAL DESIGN. **2** LOGIC DESIGN.

destructive read A read operation that erases the stored information.

destructive readout Destructive read.

detail file A TRANSACTION FILE.

development time The part of OPERATING TIME during which new routines or hardware are bebugged.

device control character Any of various characters used to control ancillary or peripheral devices connected with a data processing or telecommunication system.

device independence A capability by means of which input/output operations can be requested independently of the characteristics of the associated devices.

DFT *abbr.* DIAGNOSTIC FUNCTION TEST.

diagnostic **1** *adj.* Of, performing, or having to do with the detection and isolation of MALFUNCTIONS and MISTAKES. **2** *n.* A diagnostic output message.

diagnostic function test A program designed to test the overall reliability of a system.

diagnostic routine In computer maintenance,

a routine designed to expose and isolate malfunctions or mistakes.

diagram *n.* A BLOCK DIAGRAM; a FUNCTIONAL DIAGRAM; a LOGIC DIAGRAM; or a VENN DIAGRAM.

dial exchange An exchange in which each subscriber can initiate calls by dialing.

dial pulse Any of the interruptions produced in the dc loop of a calling telephone by the opening and closing of the dial contacts, the interruptions occurring once for each unit of the digit dialed.

dial-up The initiation of a station-to-station call by means of a dial or pushbutton telephone.

dibit *n.* A set composed of two bits, capable of representing the four states 00, 01, 101, 11.

dichotomizing search A BINARY SEARCH.

dictionary *n.* A RELOCATION DICTIONARY.

differential *n.* Either of a pair of symbols dy, dx associated with the functional relationship y = f(x) in such a way that

$$dy/dx = f'(x) \quad \text{or} \quad dy = f'(x)dx.$$

Thus it appears that when dy/dx is used as the notation for a derivative it may be treated as a fraction. While this gives consistent results in some circumstances, it is in general not true.

differential analyzer An ANALOG COMPUTER in which DIFFERENTIAL EQUATIONS are solved by means of a network of INTEGRATORS.

differential equation An equation in which derivatives or differentials of an unknown function appear. The solution of such an equation, if it can be found, is a function, say g(x), that satisfies the equation identically throughout some interval in x. The general solution, containing one or more arbitrary constants, represents the set of functions that satisfy the equation. In physical problems, the arbitrary constants are determined from additional conditions that must be satisfied. Some differential equations have singular solutions that are not part of the general solution. Differential equations result from mathematical descriptions of motion and change.

differential gear A device that relates the angular displacement of three shafts, generally in such a way that the algebraic sum of the rotation of one pair of shafts is equal to twice the rotation of the third, often used to perform addition and subtraction in analog computers.

differentiate *v.* **1** To distinguish. **2** To find the derivative of (a function). **3** To deliver an output that is the derivative with respect to time of (the input). — **differentiation** *n.*

differentiator *n.* A device whose output is proportional (or very nearly so) to the derivative of its input with respect to one or more variables, in particular, an electric network in which the input $X_1(t) = v(t)$ results in the output $X_2(t) \cong v'(t)$, where v is voltage and t time.

digit *n.* In a number system based on m, that is, in a system in which an arbitrary positive integer is represented in the form

$$q = \sum_{i=0}^{n} c_i m^i {}_3$$

any of the set of characters representing the possible values of c_i, that is, the set of integers

$$\{0, 1, 2, \cdots m - 1\}.$$

digital *adj.* **1** Of or having to do with digits. **2** Indicating data that is expressed as a set of digits.

digital computer A computer that processes information in numerical or coded form, rather than in the form of directly measurable quantities. Compare ANALOG COMPUTER.

digital converter A device that puts information into digital form.

digital data Data that is represented in the form of discrete symbols rather than in continuous form.

digital differential analyzer A device in which digital representation and data-handling techniques are applied to the solution of differential equations.

digital signal A signal that represents digital data, generally one in which various states are represented by discrete levels of some physical parameter.

digital subset A DATA SET (def. 1).

digitize *v.* To convert (data) from analog form to digital form.

digit place In the positional representation of a number, the position in which a digit is located and, hence, the power of the chosen radix by which it is to be multiplied.

digit punch On a punched card, a punch in any of the rows representing 0–9, the 0 punch also functioning as a ZONE PUNCH in alphabetic representation.

diminished-radix complement A RADIX-MINUS-ONE COMPLEMENT.

diode *n.* A two-terminal device in which current is a nonlinear function of voltage, and whose characteristic is markedly asymmetrical with respect to the point where voltage equals zero. Diodes are often designed to have other special characteristics as well.

diode logic A form of digital circuitry in which logic is performed by varying the biases on diodes so that they turn on and off.

diplexer *n.* A coupling device that allows two radio transmitters to share the same antenna.

direct access RANDOM ACCESS.

direct access device A RANDOM ACCESS DEVICE.

direct address An address that serves to indicate the location of an operand.

direct distance dialing A telephone exchange service by means of which a subscriber can direct calls to other subscribers that are not in his local service area without requiring assistance from an operator.

direct insertion subroutine An OPEN SUBROUTINE.

director *n.* In common-carrier telegraph systems, an equipment set that makes cross-office selection and input-to-output line connection as specified by addresses contained in the message.

direct-point repeater In a telegraph system, an arrangement in which a relay controlled by received signals generates corresponding signals onto another line or lines without the action of any other transmitting or repeating device.

disaster dump A dump that occurs as the result of a non-recoverable program error.

disc *n.* A MAGNETIC DISC.

disc storage A form of storage in which information is recorded as tracks of magnetic pulses on rotating discs.

disconnect *v.* To remove (apparatus) from a particular connection and restore it to a condition in which it is ready for use.

disconnect signal A signal originated at one end of a subscriber line or trunk in order to indicate to equipment at the other end that the connection now established is to be disconnected.

discrete programming INTEGER PROGRAMMING.

disk *n.* A DISC.

disk storage DISC STORAGE.

dispatching priority In a multitask situation, a number assigned to each task to indicate its relative precedence for use of the central processing unit.

display *n.* A representation of data in visual form.

display tube An electron tube, generally a cathode-ray tube, used to provide a display.

display unit A device designed to produce a display.

dissector *n.* An IMAGE DISSECTOR.

distance *n.* SIGNAL DISTANCE.

distortion *n.* Any undesired change in a signal waveform.

distributing frame A structure used to terminate the permanent wires of a telephone central office, private exchange, or private branch exchange, while allowing facility in the change of connections.

distribution cable Any of the branches from a FEEDER CABLE.

dividend *n.* In division, the number whose multiplicative inverse is to be determined, specifically, in the examples given under DIVISION, the number c.

division *n.* The determination of the number that is the multiplicative inverse of another number with respect to a third number. More explicitly, given a trio of numbers a, b, c, where $c = a \times b$, division is the process of finding a when b and c are given, or of finding b when a and c are given.

divisor *n.* In division, the number with respect to which the multiplicative inverse of another number is to be determined, specifically, in the examples given under DIVISION, the number *b* in the first case and *a* in the second.

DLE *abbr.* The DATA LINK ESCAPE CHARACTER.

DLT *abbr.* DATA LOOP TRANSCEIVER.

document *n.* **1** A data medium and any data recorded on it in a form that is directly usable by human beings. **2** Any permanent record that can be read by a human being or a machine.

documentation *n.* **1** The origination, amassing, storage, reference to, and distribution of documents or the information contained therein. **2** A corpus of documents or data pertaining to a particular subject.

documentor *n.* A routine designed to produce and maintain program flowcharts, text material, and other tabular or graphic information.

document reference edge In character recognition, a document edge with respect to which character alignment is defined.

domain *n.* For a FUNCTION, the set of all possible values of an independent variable.

DOS *abbr.* Disk OPERATING SYSTEM.

dot cycle One cycle of a periodic alternation between two signaling conditions, each of unit duration. Telegraph transmission speed when measured in dot cycles per second is equal to one half the rate as expressed in BAUDS.

dot speed Telegraph transmission speed as measured in DOT CYCLES per second.

double length DOUBLE PRECISION.

double precision Indicating a number that is represented in the form of two computer words and thus has twice the PRECISION of a number represented as a single word.

double pulse recording A form of magnetic recording in which each storage cell is composed of a pair of regions magnetized with opposite polarity and bounded by unmagnetized regions, the sense of each bit (0 or 1) being determined by the order in which the magnetized regions occur.

double punch On a HOLLERITH CARD, more than one NUMERIC PUNCH in any single column.

double rail logic Indicating self-timed asynchronous circuits in which every logic variable is represented by a pair of electrical lines which can, jointly, take on three meaningful states.

downtime *n.* The time during which a device is unavailable for use as a result of malfunctions.

drive *n.* A TAPE DRIVE.

drop *n.* A SUBSCRIBER'S DROP.

drop in The acceptance of a spurious signal by virtue of the fact that its amplitude exceeds a predetermined percentage of the nominal signal amplitude.

drop out **1** On a magnetic tape, a signal whose amplitude is less than that of a reference signal by a specified percentage. **2** In data transmission, a received signal that results from the effects of noise or faults in the system.

drum *n.* A MAGNETIC DRUM.

drum mark On a magnetic drum, a character that indicates the end of a record.

drum storage An information-storage device consisting of a rotating cylinder coated with magnetic material. Data is stored in a number of tracks, each served by its own record/play-back head.

dry contact A portion of an electric circuit that contains only resistive components and contact points.

dry reed contact A REED RELAY.

DS *abbr.* A DATA SET.

DTR *abbr.* Distribution tape reel.

dual operators Either of a pair of logic operators each of which is equivalent to the NOT of the other when applied to the NOT of its operands. More explicitly, let F_1, F_2 be two logic operations, let A, B be two operands, and let the symbol ' denote NOT; then F_1 is the dual of F_2 if and only if $F_1(A, B) = F_2'(A', B')$. For example, since $(A + B) = (A' \cdot B')'$, in words, A OR B is equivalent to NOT(NOT A AND NOT B), the operators AND and OR ($\cdot$ and $+$) are duals.

dummy *adj.* Simulating some of the characteristics of another object without actually functioning as such: a *dummy* antenna; a *dummy* load.

dump **1** *v.* To copy the information contained in all or part of (a storage), the process usually proceeding from an internal storage to an external storage. **2** *n.* The process of dumping. **3** *n.* The mass of data resulting from a dump.

duodecimal *adj.* **1** Indicating a property that involves a choice in which there are 12 possibilities. **2** Of or having to do with the system of numeration that uses 12 as its radix.

duplex *adj.* Indicating a communications system in which messages can proceed in both directions at once.

duplicate *v.* To copy in such a way that the result is identical with the source in physical form as well as in data content. Compare COPY.

duplication check A check in which the same task is performed independently two or more times and the results compared.

dyadic Boolean operator A Boolean operator that is applied to a pair of operands, specifically, the operators AND, equivalence, exclusive OR, inclusion, NAND, NOR, and OR.

dyadic operation An operation that is performed on a pair of operands.

dynamic dump A DUMP performed while a program is being executed.

dynamic programming In operations research, an optimization procedure that contains a number of stages. While there may be at each stage of the procedure a number of alternatives which seem equally good, it is, in general, necessary to evaluate the consequences of each alternative through the stages which follow it.

dynamic storage A data-storage device in which the data or their locations vary with time in such a way that a specified item may or may not be available for immediate recovery.

dynamic storage allocation A storage allocation technique in which storage areas are assigned according to criteria applied at the time when the storage is needed.

dynamic subroutine A subroutine that is generalized with respect to certain of its parameters, these being particularized or adjusted in accordance with the requirements of the main routine at the time of use.

E

EAM *abbr.* ELECTRICAL ACCOUNTING MACHINE.

EAX *abbr.* ELECTRONIC AUTOMATIC EXCHANGE.

EBCDIC *abbr.* Extended Binary Coded Decimal Interchange Code.

echo check A method in which the accuracy of transmitted data is checked by returning them to the sending end for comparison with the source data.

echo suppressor On a transmission line, a device that prevents signals from being reflected to the transmitter end.

edge *n.* **1** A DOCUMENT REFERENCE EDGE. **2** A STROKE EDGE.

edit *v.* To adjust the form or format of (data), for example, to perform zero suppression and insert decimal points.

edit control character An ACCURACY CONTROL CHARACTER.

EDP *abbr.* Electronic Data Processing.

effective address An address derived from a specified address by the application of whatever indexing or indirect addressing rules are in effect, and which serves to identify a current operand.

effective speed Of a data transmission system, a speed derived by adjusting the nominal speed downward to allow for the effects of control codes, error detection, retransmission, timing codes, etc.

EIA *abbr.* Electronic Industries Association.

EIA interface A set of signal parameters (duration and impedance level) specified by the Electronic Industries Association for connections between business machines and data sets.

eight-level code A code in which eight impulses are used to describe a single character, with additional "start" and "stop" elements sometimes used for asynchronous transmission. See USASCII.

electrical accounting machine Any of the various data-processing machines that are electromechanical rather than electronic in nature, as, for instance, a keypunch or a collating machine.

electromagnetic delay line A delay line composed of a network of lumped impedances.

electronic *adj.* Of or having to do with the field of electronics or its principles.

Electronic Automatic Exchange Electronic telephone exchange equipment: a term used by General Telephone Co.

electronic data processing Data processing that is carried out largely by means of devices that are electronic in nature.

electronics *n.* **1** The branch of science and engineering that deals with the design, manufacture, and utilization of machines that operate by controlled electrical conduction, as by means of vacuum tubes, semiconductor devices, etc. **2** The electronic parts of a system or device, as contrasted with the mechanical or other parts.

Electronic Switching System An electronic switching device developed by the Bell System to handle central office functions.

electrostatic storage A device that stores data in the form of electrically charged regions on a dielectric surface.

EM *abbr.* The END OF MEDIUM CHARACTER.

embossment *n.* **1** A deformation of the surface of a document. **2** In character recognition, the distance between the nondeformed part of a document surface and a specified point on a printed character.

emergency maintenance CORRECTIVE MAINTE-NANCE.

emulate *v.* To operate a data-processing system in such a way that it acts in a manner identical to that of another such system, that is, to cause it to accept the same forms of data and execute the same programs as does the other system.

emulator *n.* A device or routine used in emulation.

encode *v.* To represent (data) in a code.

end-around carry A carry that propagates from the highest-order place to the lowest-order place.

end-around shift A shift operation in which bits dropped from the low-order position of a word are reintroduced in the high-order position or vice versa.

end distortion In a teletypewriter circuit, the displacement of the trailing edges of the marking pulses from their correct positions with respect to the leading edge of the start pulse.

end office A class 5 office of a local telephone exchange in which a subscriber's loop terminates.

end-of-file mark A control character indicating that the last record of a file has been read.

end-of-medium character A control character that indicates that either the physical end of the data medium or the end of the portion of the data medium upon which desired data is recorded has been reached.

end of message A character or sequence of characters that indicates the end of a message or record.

end-of-tape marker On a magnetic tape, anything that marks the end of the permissible recording area.

end-of-text character In data communication, a control character that indicates the end of a text.

end of transmission In data communication, a character or sequence of characters that indicates the end of a particular transmission.

end-of-transmission-block character In a data communication situation where data has been arranged in blocks for transmission, a control character that indicates the end of a block.

end-of-transmission character In data communication, a control character that indicates a cessation of transmission.

energy level diagram A graph that shows the levels (or relative levels) of signal power at various points in a communications channel.

ENQ *abbr.* The enquiry character.

enquiry character In data communications, a control character used to elicit a response from a remote station, requesting, in general, station identification and, sometimes, description of the station equipment and status.

Enterprise number In telephone service, an exchange number by means of which the called party is automatically billed for incoming calls.

entry conditions For a given routine, the initial data and control conditions necessary for its successful execution.

entry point Any point in a routine to which control can be passed.

EOM *abbr.* END OF MESSAGE.

EOT *abbr.* **1** The END OF TRANSMISSION CHARACTER. **2** END OF TRANSMISSION.

equalization *n.* In general, any form of compensation for undesirable frequency response or phase response in a communications system.

equalizer *n.* A passive or active network, generally composed of lumped impedances, and designed to provide equalization.

equal sign **1** In mathematics, the sign $=$, used to indicate that a pair of quantities or expressions are equal. **2** In FORTRAN and certain other programming languages, the sign $=$, used to indicate that the quantity on the left of it is to be set equal to the quantity on the right. For example, consider the statement $X = X + Y$. Interpreted according to the rules of algebra, the statement is nonsense unless Y is equal to zero. In FORTRAN, however, the statement is interpreted to mean, "The new value of X is to be made equal to the current value of X plus the current value of Y."

equation *n.* In mathematics, a statement that two quantities or expressions are equal. In general, if variables are present, the values for which this condition holds true are not necessarily known. Compare IDENTITY.

equipment *n.* PERIPHERAL EQUIPMENT.

equivalence *n.* A relation (here denoted as $*$) defined on a set S in the following way: Let s, t, u be three arbitrary members of S; if (1) $s*s$, and (2) $s*t$ implies $t*s$, and (3) $s*t$ and $t*u$ together imply that $s*u$, then the relation $*$ is that of equivalence. For the purposes of data processing and logic S is normally a set of statements.

equivalent binary digits The number of binary places required to express the number of elements contained in a given set.

equivalent four-wire system A transmission system in which duplex operation is obtained over a single pair of wires by means of multiplex techniques.

erase *v.* To destroy or clear (the information recorded in a storage medium).

erase character The DELETE CHARACTER.

erase head On a magnetic tape drive, a magnetic head designed solely to erase old information from the tape before new information is written.

ERR *abbr.* ERROR.

error *n.* The deviation of an observed or computed result from a theoretically correct or true result; also, the extent or cause of such deviation.

error burst In data transmission, a sequence of bits in which one or more is erroneous, the entire sequence being counted as a single unit in accordance with some prearranged criterion.

error control character An ACCURACY CONTROL CHARACTER.

error-correcting code A code constructed in such a way that the representation for each character contains a number of redundant bits, allowing the character to be correctly recognized if certain of the bits are erroneously transmitted.

error-detecting code A code in which the representation for each character contains a set number of redundant bits that make all the representations conform to a common rule of construction, deviation from this rule being taken as evidence of an erroneously transmitted character.

error message A message indicating that an error has been detected.

error range The interval bounded by the least and greatest error values.

error rate A figure of merit for a circuit or system, frequently given as the number of erroneous bits or characters received per 100,000 transmitted.

error ratio The ratio of erroneous data units received to the total number transmitted.

error routine A routine to which control is passed and which takes any of various corrective actions when an error is recognized.

error signal In a control system, a signal that is proportional to the difference between the desired value of the controlled variable and its actual value.

ESC *abbr.* The ESCAPE CHARACTER.

escape character A code character that together with one or more succeeding characters forms an ESCAPE SEQUENCE.

escape sequence In the transmission of coded data, a sign that an indicated sequence of bits is to be interpreted according to a different code.

ESD *abbr.* EXTERNAL SYMBOL DICTIONARY.

ESS *abbr.* ELECTRONIC SWITCHING SYSTEM.

estimator *n.* In statistics, a function $f(t) = x$, used in preparing a set of estimates of the value of x as t is varied within its domain.

ETB *abbr.* The END OF TRANSMISSION BLOCK CHARACTER.

ETX *abbr.* The END OF TEXT CHARACTER.

event *n.* **1** An operation performed on data or something that happens in preparation for such an operation. **2** Any happening that generates data.

excess three code A binary coded decimal notation in which an arbitrary decimal digit N is represented by the binary equivalent of $N + 3$.

exchange *n.* **1** A unit established by a communications common carrier for the operation of communications in a specified geographical area, containing, in general, one or more central offices and their associated equipment. **2** A CENTRAL OFFICE.

exchange buffering A technique that uses data chaining to eliminate the need to move data about in main storage, the control of buffer segments and user program work areas being passed between the user program and the data management routine on the basis of need and availability.

exchange, classes of Class 1, a REGIONAL CENTER; Class 2, a SECTIONAL CENTER; Class 3, a PRIMARY CENTER; Class 4, a TOLL CENTER; Class 5, an END OFFICE.

exchange system A system in which the stations of any two customers can be interconnected by means of an exchange.

exclusion *n.* A logic operator having the property that if P, Q, and X are statements, and X is equivalent to P exclusion Q, then X is true whenever P is true and Q is false; more compactly, $X = P \cdot Q'$, where $\cdot$ denotes AND and $'$ denotes NOT.

exclusive OR A logical operator having the property that if P, Q, and X are statements, and X is equivalent to P exclusive OR Q, then X is true if P is true or Q is true, but false if both P and Q are true or false. More compactly, $X = (P + Q) \cdot (P \cdot Q)'$, where $+$ denotes OR, $\cdot$ denotes AND, and $'$ denotes NOT.

Truth table for
EXCLUSIVE OR operator

A	B	$A \oplus \cdot B^*$
0	0	0
0	1	1
1	0	1
0	0	0

* Symbolic notation for A **EXCLUSIVE OR** B,
equivalent to (A AND NOT B) OR (B AND NOT A)

exclusive segments Two segments in the same region of an overlay program, neither of which is in the path of the other, and which, consequently, cannot be in main storage at the same time.

EXEC *abbr.* The EXECUTE STATEMENT.

execute *v.* **1** To carry out (an instruction). **2** To perform (a routine).

execute statement A job control statement that identifies a load module to be fetched and executed, thus specifying a job step.

executive routine A routine designed to control and expedite the execution of other routines.

expandor *n.* A device whose operation is the inverse of that of a compressor, used, in general, to restore a compressed signal to its original form.

exponent *n.* **1** A number indicating the POWER to which a number or expression is to be raised. **2** In floating-point representation, a CHARACTERISTIC.

exponential function A function of the form $f(x) = kb^z$, where k, b are constants.

expression *n.* A combination of operations and operands written in a SOURCE LANGUAGE.

extended area service A type of telephone exchange service which in return for a somewhat higher exchange service rate serves an extended area in which there is a community of interest without toll charges.

extension *n.* **1** On the premises of a subscriber, any additional equipment connected to the same line but at a location remote from the main station. **2** Any of the telephones served by a PRIVATE BRANCH EXCHANGE.

extension station Any additional telephone set connected to a subscriber line by means of an extension and having the same call number designation as the main station with which it is associated.

extent *n.* On input/output devices, the actual physical locations that are occupied by or reserved for a particular data set.

external clocking See DATA SET CLOCKING.

external reference A reference to a symbol defined in another module.

external storage A storage device, as cards or tape, external to the computer itself but capable of storing information in a form accessible to the computer.

external symbol Any symbol, as a control section name, entry point name, external reference, or the like, stored in the EXTERNAL SYMBOL DICTIONARY.

external symbol dictionary A compilation of control information associated with an object or load module in such a way as to identify the external symbols in the module.

extract *v.* To separate or remove (a part of a word) from a whole word or (a specific item) from a file.

extract instruction An instruction directing that a new expression be formed from designated parts of other expressions.

F

facility *n.* That which is available for use, especially a communications path or anything used in furnishing communications service.

facsimile *n.* A method of transmitting pictures, maps, etc., by radio or wire. The image is scanned at the transmitter and reconstructed at the receiving station.

facsimile signal level The maximum signal power or voltage produced by the scanning of a given subject copy as measured at any point in a facsimile system, corresponding to picture white or picture black depending on the system of modulation used.

factor *n.* **1** Any of a set of quantities whose product is a given quantity. **2** A SCALE FACTOR.

factorial *n.* An operator that applies to a number in the following way: if *n* is the number under consideration, then *n* factorial (written *n*!) is equal to $n \times (n - 1) \times (n - 2) \ldots \times 1$, it being understood by convention that $0! = 1$.

factorial sign The sign ! placed after a number to indicate that it is a FACTORIAL.

false add The formation of a partial sum, that is, an add operation in which no carries are used.

false retrieval In an automatic library search, any retrieved item that is vaguely related but not pertinent to the subject of the search.

family *n.* In mathematics, a set of functions, curves, etc., that can be generated by varying one or more of the parameters of a general form, thus if

$$G(x, y) = g(x, y, P_1, P_2, \ldots, P_n),$$

a *k*-parameter family of functions is the set of all $G(x, y)$ that result when *k* members of the set $P_1, P_2, \ldots, P_n$ are allowed to take all possible values.

fan-in The number of inputs that a logic circuit can accommodate.

fan-out The ability of the output of a logic circuit to drive other such circuits.

far-end crosstalk Crosstalk that traverses a circuit in the same direction as the desired signals.

fault *n.* Any physical condition that causes a device, system, etc., to fail to meet its designed performance specifications.

FAX *abbr.* FACSIMILE.

FCC *abbr.* FEDERAL COMMUNICATIONS COMMISSION.

FD *or* **FDX** *abbr.* Full DUPLEX.

FDM *abbr.* FREQUENCY DIVISION MULTIPLEX.

FE *abbr.* The FORMAT EFFECTOR CHARACTER.

Federal Communications Commission Under the Communications Act of 1934, a board of seven commissioners empowered to regulate all interstate communications and foreign communications that originate in the United States.

feedback *n.* The return of a part of a system output to the system input, causing, in general, a profound change in the characteristics of the system. If the returned signal is in phase with the input, it is called **positive or regenerative feedback**; if it is out of phase it is called **negative or degenerative feedback**. Negative feedback improves the stability and linearity of a system at the expense of GAIN, while positive feedback increases gain and speed of response but makes the system less stable and more oscillatory. Consider an amplifier having gain A_0 and distortion B_0, both, in general, complex numbers. It can be shown that via the introduction of a feedback network β the gain A_f and distortion B_f of the new closed loop system are made different from the original open loop parameters. In particular

$$A_f = A_0/(1 - \beta A_0), \quad B_f = B_0/(1 - \beta A_0).$$

Thus, provided that $|1 - A_0| > 1$, the closed loop system will have lower gain and distortion. It can also be shown that the input impedance is increased and the output impedance decreased, both by the factor $1 - \beta A_0$. Further, since

$$dA_f/A_f = dA_0/A_0[1/(1 - \beta A_0)],$$

a change in open loop gain affects closed loop gain but slightly. For a system intended to oscillate sufficient positive feedback must be used so that $1 - \beta A_0 = 0$.

feedback control system A system containing a set of devices that measure its output or outputs against an appropriate set of reference signals, generating a set of error signals which in turn control the system in such a way that its outputs conform to desired performance criteria. The performance, that is, the ratio between output c and reference r, of the generalized system shown is given by

$$c/r = KHG/(1 + KFHG).$$

The system becomes unstable if $1 + KFGH = 0$, that is, if the phase shift around the loop H-K-G-F is zero when $|KHFG| = 1$. See FEED-BACK.

feedback loop In a system using FEEDBACK, the LOOP that connects the output and input.

feedback system **1** A FEEDBACK CONTROL SYSTEM. **2** An INFORMATION FEEDBACK SYSTEM.

feeder cable The main cable from a central office.

feed holes In a paper tape, the holes punched in order to allow a sprocket wheel to drive it.

ferrite *n.* Any of various, often magnetic chemical compounds that contain ferric oxide (Fe_2O_3). The principal ferrites are of the form MFe_2O_4, where M is a divalent metal. Ferrites have high magnetic permeability and high electrical resistivity; thus when used as CORES their eddy-current losses are low.

fetch *v.* To retrieve and load (information) from a storage device.

FF *abbr.* The FORM FEED CHARACTER.

F format A data set record format in which the logic records are all of the same length.

field *n.* In a record, a specified area reserved for data of a particular type, as, for instance, a number of bits in a machine instruction that indicate the operation code.

Fieldata code A standard military data code in which each character is represented by 7 data bits and one parity bit.

FIGS *abbr.* A FIGURES SHIFT.

figurative constant In a programming language, a fixed, preassigned string of characters with a fixed, preassigned data name.

figures shift In a teletypewriter, a physical movement that allows numbers, symbols, upper case characters, and the like to be printed.

file *n.* A set of records that are in some way related and treated, collectively, as a unit.

file gap In a data storage medium, an area intended primarily to indicate the end of a FILE and, possibly, the beginning of another.

file layout The configuration of data in a FILE.

file maintenance Any addition to, change of, or deletion from the data in a FILE in order to keep it up to date.

file separator character A control character designed to establish a logical boundary between FILES.

film *n.* A MAGNETIC THIN FILM.

filter *n.* **1** A device, program, etc. that divides a set of data, signals, or other material into two or more subsets defined by specified properties. **2** A MASK.

FINAC *abbr.* Fast Interline Non-active Automatic Control. (A leased automatic teletypewriter service provided by American Telephone & Telegraph.)

fine index The more specific of a pair of indices consulted in order to gain access to a particular record.

first-generation computer A computer designed around vacuum-tube technology.

five-level code A telegraph code, as for example Baudot code, that uses five impulses in the specification of each character, with, often, "start" and "stop" elements added for asynchronous transmission.

fixed-cycle operation Any operation whose completion always requires an exact, specified number of regularly timed execution cycles.

fixed-length record Indicating a file in which every record must be of the same specified length.

fixed-point Indicating a method or system in which each number is represented by a set number of digits, the radix point being located by implication in a particular position with respect to those digits.

fixed-point arithmetic Arithmetic that is performed on fixed-point numbers exclusively.

fixed-point number A number that is represented in FIXED-POINT form.

fixed-point part A MANTISSA.

fixed-point representation Any form of numerical representation in which a FIXED-POINT convention is used.

fixed-radix notation A form of POSITIONAL NOTATION in which the multiplier applied to each digit place is an integral power of the same radix, the places generally being arranged in order of the powers, with the most significant digit place at the left.

fixed storage A storage device in which the data contained cannot be altered by means of computer instructions.

fixed word-length computer A computer in which all data is handled in units composed of a fixed number of bits or characters. Compare VARIABLE WORD-LENGTH COMPUTER.

flag *n.* Any of various indicators used to identify a particular condition or occurrence, an example being a character that identifies the beginning or end of a word, field, or the like.

flip-flop A BISTABLE electronic circuit or other device.

floating-point Indicating a system of numeration in which the position of the radix point with respect to the numerals is variable.

floating-point arithmetic Arithmetic performed exclusively on FLOATING-POINT NUMBERS.

floating-point base In floating-point representation (def. 2), the invariant positive integer taken to be the base to which the indicated exponent is applied.

floating-point number A number expressed in floating-point representation.

floating-point radix A FLOATING-POINT BASE.

floating-point representation 1 A system of numerical representation in which the position of the radix point with respect to the numeral is variable. 2 A system of numerical representation in which each number is represented as a fixed-point number (with the radix point understood to be at the right of the digits) multiplied by an integral power of a fixed radix, for example 472–08 might represent 472×10^{-8}.

flow *n.* In data processing, a concept referring to the order or sequence in which events occur or operations are performed. See FLOWCHART.

flowchart *n.* A schematic representation of some aspect of a problem, that is, its definition, analysis, solution, or the like, in which various symbols represent hardware, data, flow, operations, etc. See DATA FLOWCHART.

flow direction In flowcharting, the relation, indicated by arrows or other conventions, that determines which of a pair of operations is the successor of the other.

flowline *n.* On a flowchart, a line that indicates a FLOW.

fluidics *n.* The branch of engineering and technology concerned with the design and production of logic elements, amplifiers, and the like, that depend for their operation on interactions between jets of fluid rather than on electrical phenomena. While slower than electronic logic systems, fluid logic systems can operate in environments that would damage electronic systems.

flying-spot scanner In optical character recognition, a device in which a spot of light scans a sample space according to a predetermined pattern, a signal corresponding to the intensity of the light transmitted or reflected at each point being developed by means of a photoelectric transducer.

font *n.* A set of characters of a particular size and style, especially a TYPE FONT.

forbidden combination An invalid combination of bits or other representations. Compare ILLEGAL CHARACTER.

foreground processing The automatic execution of the programs, often REAL-TIME programs, that have been assigned the highest priorities for the use of the machine. Compare BACKGROUND PROCESSING.

foreign exchange service A telephone service by means of which a customer can be connected with a central office that does not normally serve his location.

formal logic The study of the form and structure of logically valid statements without regard to content.

format *n.* A particularized order or arrangement of data, as an ADDRESS FORMAT.

format effector Any of various control characters designed to layout or position information to a printing or display device.

form feed character A format effector that determines the point at which a printing or display device moves to the next page, form, or its equivalent.

FORTRAN For(mula) Tran(slating System), any of several procedure-oriented programming languages designed mainly for scientific or mathematical problems.

fortuitous distortion A form of telegraph distortion in which the transmitted pulses are randomly varied in duration.

four-address Of, indicating, or having to do with an instruction format in which there are four address parts.

four-phase modulation A form of modulation in which the carrier is shifted between four distinct phases, the four possible phases serving to encode two bits.

four-plus-one address Of, indicating, or having to do with an instruction that contains four operand addresses and one control address.

four-row keyboard The keyboard used in certain types of teletypewriter equipment. Compare THREE-ROW KEYBOARD.

four-wire circuit A duplex communications circuit in which a station is connected to one pair of wires for each direction of transmission.

four-wire repeater A repeater designed for use in a four-wire circuit and, therefore, containing two amplifiers.

four-wire terminating set A hybrid arrangement by which four-wire circuits are terminated on a two-wire basis for interconnection with TWO-WIRE CIRCUITS.

fox message A standard test message for telegraph systems, containing all of the alphamerics and most of the function characters. The message is: THE QUICK BROWN FOX JUMPED OVER A LAZY DOG'S BACK 12345-67890 (STATION NAME) SENDING.

fraction *n.* **1** A number that is expressed as the explicit or implied quotient of two other numbers. **2** A part of some defined whole.

frame *n.* **1** A row of bit or punched positions extending across a paper or magnetic tape in a direction perpendicular to its movement. **2** A MAIN FRAME.

frame, type A A distributing frame carrying on one side (horizontally) all outside lines and their associated protective devices and on the other side (vertically) the terminations of the central office equipment and their associated protective devices.

frame, type B A distributing frame similar to a type A frame except that the relative orientations (horizontal and vertical) of the outside lines and central office equipment terminations are reversed.

framing *n.* The process of dividing a continuous stream of bits into the groupings representing one or more characters.

framing bits Any of the bits which, while they carry no information per se, make possible the separation of characters in a bit stream.

free routing A method of traffic handling in which messages are sent to their destinations via any available channels rather than by predetermined routes.

frequency *n.* The number of occurrences of a

periodic phenomenon, as oscillation, per unit of time, usually expressed in HERTZ (cycles per second).

frequency division multiplex A technique whereby the total BANDWIDTH of a communications channel is divided into two or more smaller BANDS each of which can be used for transmitting a message.

frequency modulation A form of MODULATION in which the frequency of the carrier is made to vary in accordance with the information to be transmitted, that is, given a carrier

$$C(t) = A \cos (\omega_0 t + \phi),$$

and an INFORMATION FUNCTION $g(t)$, the signal transmitted is

$$C_m(t) = A \cos [(\omega_0 + g(t) - \Delta\omega)(t) + \phi].$$

When used for communications this system has the advantages of greater immunity from noise and other interference, at the cost of increased bandwidth.

frequency-shift keying A form of frequency modulation in which the INFORMATION FUNCTION is a digital signal.

FS *abbr.* File separator character.

FSK *abbr.* Frequency-shift keying.

FTS *abbr.* Federal Telecommunications System.

full duplex DUPLEX.

full speed The maximum rated speed of a transmission system.

fully perforated tape Paper tape that is perforated in such a way that chads are produced, that is, in which a complete hole is made.

function *n.* 1 An association between a pair of variables such that for every possible value of the first, the independent variable, there corresponds a unique value of the second, the dependent variable. More generally, a function may relate any number of independent variables to one dependent variable. If for a given function G,

$$- G(x) = G(- x),$$

G is said to be an odd function; if

$$G(x) = G(- x).$$

G is an even function. **2** The rule that indicates this correspondence: the sine *function*; an exponential *function*. **3** The value of the dependent variable: y is a *function of x*. Modern mathematical practice generally insists that a function be single-valued. Consider the relation

$$y = \sqrt{x}.$$

For any value of x, say x_0, there are two possible values of y, namely y_0 and $- y_0$. This is not a satisfactory definition of a function unless the restriction $0 \leq y$ is made, that is, we must exclude negative values of y. Also a function need not be defined for every value of the independent variable. Thus

$$f(x) = (x + 3)^5/(x - 1)^2$$

is not defined when its denominator is zero, that is, when $x = 1$. **4** The activity or purpose a system or device is designed to carry on or fulfill. **5** In communications, any of various particular machine actions.

functional diagram A graphical representation of the relationships among the parts of a system in terms of their various functions.

function generator An electrical network that can be adjusted to make its output voltage (or current) a desired function of time, used in conjunction with analog computers.

function key On a keyboard, a key that initiates some mechanical function in a receiving device necessary to the reception of a message in its proper form.

function table **1** A table that lists a set of values for one or more independent variables together with the associated set of values of the independent variable. See FUNCTION. **2** A device or subroutine that can decode multiple inputs into a single output or perform the inverse operation of this.

G

gain *n.* In communications, an increase in signal power as measured between two points.

gang-punch To reproduce all or part of the information on one punched card onto succeeding cards.

gap *n.* A BLOCK GAP; a FILE GAP; an INTER-RECORD GAP; or a RECORD GAP.

gap scatter In a magnetic tape system, misalignment of the gaps in the read-heads that serve parallel tracks.

garbage *n.* Any meaningless and undesired configuration of bits contained in storage.

gate *n.* An electrical network or other device having multiple inputs and a single output which, except for brief switching conditions, is energized when and only when there exists a particular, defined configuration of energized inputs; a logic circuit. See AND-GATE; OR-GATE, etc.

gather write A procedure in which a computer combines data items from noncontiguous areas of storage into a single physical block or record.

generalized routine A routine designed to process a large range of specific jobs within a given type of application.

general-purpose computer A computer that is designed so far as possible to avoid limitation of its range of application.

generate *v.* To produce (a routine) by selection of subroutines from a skeletally coded set under the control of various parameters.

generation data group A collection of successive, historically related data sets.

generator *n.* A routine that controls and executes a GENERATE function.

geometric mean A special case of an average, derived from a set of numbers by multiplying them all together and extracting the root corresponding to the number of factors; more explicitly, the geometric mean G of a set of numbers $x_1, x_2, \ldots x_n$, is given by

$$G = (x_1 \cdot x_2 \cdot \ldots \cdot x_n)^{1/n}.$$

get *v.* To make (a record) from an input file available for use by the routine in control of the machine.

giga- *prefix* One billion, 10^9, times a specified unit.

GIGO *abbr.* G(arbage) i(n)-G(arbage) o(ut): a reference to the fact that the output data supplied by a computer is no more reliable than the input data supplied to it.

GM *abbr.* A GROUP MARK.

graphic *n.* Any symbol that consists of some kind of mark made on a generally flat surface, as that of paper.

graphic character A character which, unlike a CONTROL CHARACTER, is most often represented by a GRAPHIC.

Gray code A positional binary code for the representation of numbers, designed in such a way that any pair of integers whose difference is unity are represented by binary expressions that differ by one bit.

grid *n.* In optical character recognition, a system of two sets of parallel lines which intersect each other at right angles, used in the measurement and/or specification of character images.

gross index The less specific of a pair of indices consulted in order to gain access to a particular record. Compare FINE INDEX.

ground **1** *n.* In an electric circuit, a point considered to be at nominal zero potential and to which all other potentials in the circuit are referred, often, but not always, connected to the actual surface of the earth. **2** *v.* To connect to a ground.

group *n.* **1** A word. **2** In telegraphic usage, a unit composed of six successive characters.

grouped records A set of records that has been combined into a group either to conserve storage space or reduce access time.

group indicate The printing of indicative information from the first and only the first record of a group.

group mark A character that indicates the beginning or end of a set of data.

group separator character A character designed to indicate the boundaries between different groups.

GS *abbr.* The group SEPARATOR CHARACTER.

gulp *n. slang* A succession of bytes.

H

half-adder A digital circuit having one pair of inputs (A, B) and one pair of outputs (C, D), with the condition of the outputs controlled by the inputs according to the following rules:

> A-off, B-off = C-off, D-off;
> A-off, B-on = C-on, D-off;
> A-on, B-off = C-on, D-off;
> A-on, B-on = C-off, D-on.

Two such circuits can be connected to form an ADDER.

half-adjust To round by one half of the maximum value of the number base of the counter.

half duplex Indicating or having to do with a communications system in which transmission can proceed in just one direction at any one time. Compare DUPLEX.

half-speed One half of the maximum rated speed of a transmission system.

half-word A string of bits or characters that makes up half a computer word and which can be handled as a unit, having, in general, one of its boundaries in common with the word boundary.

halt instruction A machine instruction that causes execution of the program to cease.

hammer code A HAMMING CODE.

hamming code A data code in which errors can be automatically corrected.

hamming distance SIGNAL DISTANCE.

handshaking *n.* The exchange of a conventionalized set of signals between two DATA SETS when a connection is established.

hang-up *slang* 1 An unprogrammed and unexplained stop by the machine while executing a program. 2 The failure of a computer program to operate correctly.

hard copy Any permanent, visually readable machine output.

hardware *n.* The mechanical, electromechanical, and electronic components of a computer.

harmonic *n.* A sinusoidal quantity whose frequency is an integral multiple of some fundamental frequency, that is, given a quantity, $x(t)$, where

$$x(t) = A \cos (\omega t + \phi),$$

its harmonics, $h_n(x)$ are of the form

$$h_n(x) = A_n \cos (n\omega t + \phi_n),$$

where n is an integer larger than 1.

harmonic distortion A form of DISTORTION in which the output response of a system to an input sine wave contains the sine wave together with one or more of its HARMONICS.

harmonic telephone ringer See SUBMULTIPLE RINGER.

hartley *n.* A measure of INFORMATION defined as equal to the choice between 10 equally likely alternatives. One hartley can be shown to be equal to $\log_2 10$ BITS.

hash *n.* 1 A set of mappings of sets into sets, defined in such a way that representations in the target set occur in a desired distribution. 2 GARBAGE.

hash total A sum formed from one or more corresponding fields of a file and having no purpose other than for checking.

HD *abbr.* HALF-DUPLEX.

HDX *abbr.* HALF-DUPLEX.

head *n.* A MAGNETIC HEAD.

header *n.* The initial section of a message, indicating the addressee, routing, origination time, etc.

header card A card whose information content concerns the data in the cards that succeed it.

header record A record that contains common, constant, or identifying information for a succeeding set of records.

header table A HEADER RECORD.

heading *n.* In data communications, a character sequence preceded by *SOH* and used to provide address or routing information in machine-sensible form.

hertz *n.* A unit of FREQUENCY equal to one cycle per second.

heuristic *adj.* Of, indicating, or having to do with methods of problem solution that proceed largely by trial and error.

hexadecimal *adj.* 1 Of or indicating a choice that is equivalent to four bits of information, that is, one in which there are sixteen equally likely possibilities. 2 Of or indicating a system of numeration in which the radix is 16.

hexadecimal digit Usually any of the digits 1, 2, 3, 4, 5, 6, 7, 8, 9, A, B, C, D, E, F, O, used in expressing numbers to the radix 16 (written 10 in hexadecimal form).

hierarchy *n.* A set of items that is divided into subsets of different order or rank.

high-speed carry In PARALLEL ADDITION, any of various techniques for making CARRY propagation faster.

hit *n.* **1** In mechanical retrieval systems, an answer that the machine finds. **2** In file maintenance, a correct match between a detail record and a master record. **3** Any of various transient perturbations of a transmission line which can render some of the transmitted signals unintelligible.

Hollerith *n.* A data code based on a punched card containing 12 rows and, most often, 80 columns.

home loop Designating a data transfer operation that involves only the input and output units associated with the local terminal.

home record In the chaining method of file organization, the first of a chain of records.

hopper *n.* A CARD HOPPER.

horizontal tabulation character A control character that causes a printing or display unit to skip forward to the next of a set of predetermined positions on the same line.

housekeeping *n.* Any or all of the operations or routines that contribute directly to the operation of the computer but not directly to the solution of the program.

HT *abbr.* The HORIZONTAL TABULATION CHARACTER.

hue *n.* A subjective attribute of a color that corresponds to the dominant or complementary wavelength of the light that composes it. Hue determines whether a color is perceived

as red, yellow, or blue, etc. White, black, and gray are not considered hues.

hum *n.* An extraneous low-frequency signal, particularly one that is at the power-line frequency or one of its harmonics.

hunting *n.* **1** In a feedback control system, a situation in which the controlled variable oscillates about the desired value rather than stabilizing. **2** Trunk hunting.

hybrid coil In a communications circuit, a three-winding transformer connected in such a way that signals traveling in opposite directions over a two-wire path are kept separate and do not interfere with each other.

hybrid computer A data-processing machine in which data is represented in both analog form and digital form.

hybrid integrated circuit A type of integrated circuit in which the substrate is a passive material with active chips attached to its surface.

hyperbolic functions A set of functions having properties similar to those of the TRIGONOMETRIC FUNCTIONS. The relations between these functions and a hyperbola are analogous to the relations between the trigonometric functions and a circle. These functions, which can arise in the descriptions of networks are the hyperbolic sine (sinh), hyperbolic cosine (cosh), hyperbolic tangent (tanh), hyperbolic cotangent (coth), hyperbolic secant (sech), and hyperbolic cosecant (csch). Their definitions are:

$$\sinh z = \frac{(e^z - e^{-z})}{2} = z + \frac{z^3}{3!} + \frac{z^5}{5!} \cdots;$$

$$\cosh z = \frac{(e^z + e^{-z})}{2} = 1 + \frac{z^2}{2!} + \frac{z^z}{4!} \cdots;$$

$$\tan z = \sinh z / \cosh z; \coth z = 1 / \tanh z;$$

sech $z = 1/\cosh z$; csch $z = 1/\sinh z$. Furthermore, it can be shown that sinh $iz = i \sin z$ and cosh $iz = \cos z$.

hysteresis *n.* The effect of the previous history of a system on its response to an external force or influence. Usually the term refers to a magnetic effect, but it may be applied equally well to effects found in dielectrics, switching systems, etc. Consider a functional relationship between a pair of variables, (for discussion let B, magnetic induction, be the independent variable and H, magnetic field strength, be the dependent variable) such that if both are initially zero and B increases, H increases in a characteristic way until SATURATION is reached (curve $t_0 - t_1$ in illustration). If at this point B starts to decrease H decreases also but through a new set of values, finally reaching saturation in the reverse direction (curve $t_1 - t_2$). Should B increase again H increases through yet a third set of values toward the first saturated condition (curve $t_2 - t_1$). Further variation of B between these extremes results in repeated tracing out of the curve $t_2 - t_1$, $t_1 - t_2$, the hysteresis loop. If the variation of H involves a transfer of energy there is a loss proportional to the area within the loop. This is called hysteresis loss.

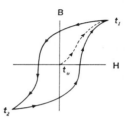

hysteresis loop See hysteresis.

hysteresis loss See hysteresis.

hz *abbr.* Hertz.

I

I/O *abbr.* Input/output.

IBM card See PUNCHED CARD; HOLLERITH.

ICA *abbr.* International Communication Association, formerly the Industrial Communication Association.

ICBS *abbr.* INTERCONNECTED BUSINESS SYSTEM.

identifier *n.* A symbol whose function is to identify a particular corpus of data.

identity *n.* In mathematics, an expression that remains true regardless of the values assigned to any variables that are present, for example, $(x + y)^2 \equiv x^2 + 2xy + y^2$ regardless of the values assigned to x and y.

identity sign In mathematics, the sign $\equiv$, used to indicate that two expressions are identical, that is that they constitute an identity rather than an EQUATION.

identity unit A gate having n signal inputs and which acts in such a way that its output signal is "on" if, and only if, all n inputs are in the same state.

idle characters Control characters that are exchanged in order to maintain synchronization between a transmitter and receiver during periods when data is not being transmitted.

idle time For an item of hardware, the portion of its AVAILABLE TIME during which no use is made of it.

IDP *abbr.* INTEGRATED DATA PROCESSING.

iff *abbr.* In logic and mathematics, if and only if.

If-then See INCLUSION.

illegal character Any character or configuration of bits that is invalid with respect to some rule or criterion.

image *n.* A CARD IMAGE.

image dissector In optical character recognition, an electronic or other transducer that divides a uniformly illuminated sample space into a number of areas, scans them in sequence, and delivers an output signal proportional to the intensity of the light received from each area.

imaginary number A number whose square is negative, that is, a number a such that $a^2 < 0$, generally written $ai = aj$, where a is any real number and $i = j = \sqrt{-1}$. See COMPLEX NUMBER.

immediate access storage A storage whose access time is so short in comparison with other systems operating as to be negligible.

immediate address Indicating an instruction that contains in an address part an actual operand rather than its address.

impedance *n.* The total opposition, in ohms, that a circuit offers to the flow of an alternating current, consisting of the combined effects of RESISTANCE R and inductive and capacitive reactance X_L, X_C. More precisely, impedance is a complex number **Z** representing the ratio of voltage **E** to current **I**. Thus

$$\mathbf{Z} = \mathbf{E}/\mathbf{I} = R + j(X_L - X_C).$$

imperative statements Those statements in a symbolic program which the assembly routine translates into actual machine-language instructions.

implication *n.* INCLUSION.

INCLUSION *n.* A logic operator defined in such a way that if P, Q, and X are statements, and X is equivalent to P INCLUSION Q, then X is true when P and Q are true, false when P is true and Q is not, and true when P is false.

Truth table for
INCLUSION operator

P	Q	P→Q*
1	1	1
1	0	0
0	1	1
0	1	1

* Symbolic notation for P **INCLUSION** Q

inclusive OR The operator OR as distinguished from EXCLUSIVE OR.

inclusive segments Overlay segments in the same region that can be in main storage at the same time.

inconnector *n.* A flowchart symbol that shows continuation of a broken flowline.

increment *n.* A change, positive or negative, in the value of a variable. For many purposes it is implicitly assumed that this change is small.

incremental computer **1** A computer in which incremental representation is the principal method used. **2** A special purpose computer designed to process increments of variables as well as their absolute values.

incremental integrator A type of digital integrator in which the output signal takes on its extreme positive or negative value or zero depending on the value of the input signal.

incremental representation A technique in which the increments in a variable are represented rather than its actual value.

index **1** *n.* An ordered listing of the items contained in a file or document, together with the information necessary to identify or gain access to those items. **2** *v.* To list (a set of items) in this manner. **3** *n.* A number or other symbol used to identify a particular member of an array of similar quantities. **4** *v.* To make a sequential set of modifications of (an address), as by means of index registers.

indexed address An address to which indexing is applied before or during the execution of an instruction.

index register A register whose contents are applied as an increment to an address, either before or during the execution of an instruction.

indicator *n.* A device or display whose condition is determined by some internal condition of the computer.

indirect address An address that identifies a storage location that contains not an operand, but another address, direct or indirect.

induction coil A device consisting of two concentric coils and an interrupter, that changes a low steady voltage into a high intermittent alternating voltage by electromagnetic induction.

infinite pad method In optical character recognition, a technique of measuring the reflectance of a paper stock in such a way that the measured reflectance is unchanged if the number of backing sheets of the same stock is doubled.

infix notation The formation of mathematical expressions by the alternation of single operands and operators, rules of operator precedence and distribution, and the use of brackets or parentheses where necessary. If it is assumed that each operator affects the operands adjacent to it and the operator $+$ takes precedence over the operator $\times$, then $A + B \times C$ translates as "A is added to B and the total multiplied by C." Compare PREFIX NOTATION.

information *n.* That property of a signal or message whereby it conveys something unpredictable by and meaningful to the recipient, usually measured in BITS.

information bits In telecommunications, the bits that are generated by the data source solely as a function of the input information, and not those used by the system for purposes of synchronization and error control.

information feedback system An information transmission system that verifies accuracy of transmission by means of an echo check.

information function A mathematical function that describes a source of information.

information processing Data processing.

information retrieval The techniques used to recover stored data.

information separator Any of various control characters designed to mark logical information boundaries.

information theory The mathematical study and analysis of the problems of encoding and decoding messages, based heavily on the science of probability. Through its ability to measure information quantitatively, this study provides criteria for evaluating the performance of communications systems.

inherited error In a sequential process, an error that originates in one stage, and is carried forward to subsequent stages.

inhibiting signal A signal that suppresses or prevents the performance of a given operation.

initialize *v.* To perform the preliminary operations necessary before the execution of a routine or a section of a routine, as, for instance, the setting of counters, switches, addresses, and the like to their beginning values.

initial program loader A routine that loads the initial section of an operating system or other program and surrenders control of the machine to the program loaded. Compare BOOT-STRAP.

initiator/terminator The job scheduler function that selects jobs and job steps for execution, allocates to them the necessary input/output devices, places them under task control, and at the completion of the job, supplies the control information for writing the job output on a system output unit.

ink *n.* MAGNETIC INK.

ink bleed In optical character recognition, the transfer of ink beyond the original boundaries of a character by capillary action.

ink smudge In optical character recognition, the transfer of ink beyond the original boundaries of a character by shear action.

ink squeezeout In optical character recognition, the transfer of ink from the center to the edges of a character during printing, resulting in a nonuniform density of the character.

inline procedures In COBOL, the procedural instructions included in the main sequential and controlling flow of a routine.

inline processing The processing of data in random order, without preliminary editing or sorting.

in-plant system A system having all its parts, including remote terminals, located in a single building or in one small area.

input *n.* **1** The information, data, signal, or the like, supplied to a system or device. **2** The energy supplied to a system or device.

input area In a storage, a section that has been reserved for input data.

input block An INPUT AREA.

input channel A channel used to convey an input to a device or system.

input data Data used or to be used as input.

input device A device or system used to convey data to another device or system.

input job stream A sequence of job control statements (which may include input data) entering a system.

input magazine A CARD HOPPER.

input/output **1** Any of the hardware used in communicating with a computer. **2** Any of the data thus communicated. **3** Any of the media in which such data are expressed.

input process **1** The reception of data by a

device. **2** The transmission of data from peripheral hardware or external storage to internal storage.

input state The condition of a specified input channel.

input work queue A QUEUE of summaries of job control statements that the JOB SCHEDULER maintains and uses to select jobs and job steps for processing.

inquiry *n.* A request that a particular item or set of items be retrieved from storage.

inquiry station That part of the equipment comprising a data terminal that can be used to originate inquiries into the system.

installation time The time spent in receiving, installing, and checking new equipment.

instruction *n.* A statement that indicates and specifies to a computer an operation to be performed and either the actual values of the operands or their addresses.

instruction address An address that gives the location of an instruction word.

instruction code An OPERATION CODE.

instruction counter A counter that indicates where the next machine instruction to be decoded and executed is located.

instruction format Any rule by which the various bits, bytes, or fields contained in an instruction are assigned various functions.

instruction register A register in which an instruction is stored for decoding and execution.

instruction repertory The set comprising all of the instructions for which a given operation code provides representations.

instruction word A word that forms part of an instruction.

integer *n.* Any of the numbers $0, \pm 1, \pm 2, \pm 3, \ldots$.

integer programming In operations research, a set of procedures used to locate the maxima and minima of a function that is subject to a set of constraints which includes one that restricts some or all of the variables to integral values.

integral **1** *n.* An operator, which operates on the continuous function $f(x)$ and is written symbolically

$$\int f(x)dx.$$

Geometrically an integral can be interpreted as the area between the curve $f(x)$ and the x axis (see illustration, page 50). In the case where the integration takes place over a finite interval $a \leq x \leq b$ the integral is termed a **definite integral** and

$$\int_a^b f(x)dx$$

equals a numerical quantity. More precisely, if the interval $[a, b]$ is divided into n subintervals Δx_i (not necessarily all equal), and an x_i is chosen in each Δx_i and a sum

$$S = \sum_{i=1}^{n} f(x_i)\Delta x_i$$

is formed, the integral

$$\int_a^b f(x)dx$$

is the limit of S as n approaches infinity in such a way that the largest x_i approaches zero, provided that this limit exists. It can be shown that $F(x)$ is the PRIMITIVE of $f(x)$, then

$$\int_a^b f(x)dx = F(b) - F(a).$$

If the integral is unbounded

$$\int f(x)dx$$

is termed an **indefinite integral**, and the result is a function of x. **2** *adj.* Of, in the form of, or having to do with an integer.

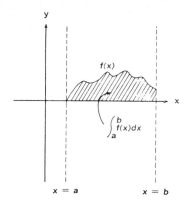

integrated circuit A small chip of solid material (generally a semiconductor) upon which, by various techniques, an array of active and/or passive components have been fabricated and interconnected to form a functioning circuit. Integrated circuits, which are generally encapsulated with only input, output, power supply, and control terminals accessible, offer great advantages in terms of small size, economy, and reliability.

integrating motor A motor designed in such a way that the angular velocity of its output shaft is proportional to its input signal, the angular displacement of the shaft being proportional to the integral with respect to time of the input signal.

integrator n. Any device whose output is proportional (or very nearly proportional) to the integral, with respect to a specified variable, of its input.

intelligence n. See ARTIFICIAL INTELLIGENCE.

interblock gap On a magnetic tape, a space left to separate two blocks of data. In general, such a space must be long enough to allow the tape transport mechanism to come to rest after the first block is read and to accelerate to operating speed in time to read the second block.

intercepting trunk A trunk to which a call directed to an invalid telephone number or a malfunctioning line is directed for action by an operator.

interception n. The routing of a call directed to an invalid telephone number or terminal address to an operator or a specially designated terminal.

intercept operator In INTERCEPTION, the operator who determines the number called and the reason for the intercept and notifies the calling party.

intercommunicating system A privately owned system capable of two-way communication without a switchboard, confined, in general, to a single building or area. All stations are capable of accepting any call, but may or may not be equipped to originate calls.

interconnected business system A system composed of a combination of smaller business systems.

interexchange channel A channel that connects two different exchange areas.

interface n. A shared boundary, as: a an item of hardware designed to make a compatible connection between two devices, or b an area of storage to which two or more programs have access.

interfix n. A technique by means of which the relationships of keywords in a document or item are described in such a way that cross-talk cannot cause false retrievals when very specific entries are made.

interior label A sequence of characters added to a magnetic tape in order to identify the contents.

interleave *v.* **1** To arrange (two or more ordered sets of objects) so that they form one master set that has the property that subsets of the original sets alternate with one another, and the ordering of the original sets is maintained. **2** To access two or more bytes or data streams (from distinct storage banks) at the same time. **3** The alternating execution of two or more operations or functions.

interlock *v.* To inhibit the initiation of operations by (a machine or device) until the operation in progress is completed.

intermediate distributing frame In a local central office, a DISTRIBUTING FRAME principally designed to cross-connect the subscriber line multiple and the subscriber line circuit.

intermediate total The sum that results when an addition process is terminated by a change of group which is neither the most nor least significant.

internal clocking NON-DATA SET CLOCKING.

internal storage Storage that is addressable by, and directly controllable by, the central processing unit of a digital computer.

International Telecommunication Union An agency of the United Nations established to provide, on a worldwide basis, standards of communication procedures and practices, including the allocation of radio frequencies.

interoffice trunk A direct trunk that connects central offices in the same exchange.

interpretation *n.* The printing on cards or paper tape of symbols equivalent to the holes punched on the same card or tape.

interpreter *n.* A routine that in sequence translates the statements of a source language program into object language instructions and executes them.

interpretive code The set of instructions comprising the source language input to an INTERPRETER.

interpretive routine A routine that decodes instructions which are written in pseudocodes and executes them immediately. Compare COMPILER.

interrecord gap A RECORD GAP.

interrupt **1** *v.* To cause (a process) to halt, especially in such a manner that it can be resumed. **2** *n.* The occurrence of an interruption.

intersection *n.* In set theory, an operator having the property that if *A* and *B* are sets the set *C* can be represented as *A* intersection *B*, if and only if every member of *C* is also a member of both *A* and *B*. This operator is closely related to the logic operator AND.

interstage punching A method of card punching in which either odd-numbered or even-numbered columns are used exclusively.

interstate *adj.* Indicating a system that has terminals located in at least two different States.

intertoll trunk A trunk that connects toll offices in different telephone exchanges.

intrastate *adj.* Completely enclosed within the boundaries of a State.

inverted file **1** In information retrieval, a cross index file organized in such a way that a keyword identifies a record. **2** A file whose normal sequence has been inverted.

inverter *n.* A circuit or other device that for an input pulse of one polarity generates an output pulse of the opposite polarity; a NOT gate.

invitation to send In Western Union terminology, a character transmitted to a remote teletypewriter terminal that polls its tape transmitter.

inward WATS A telephone service similar to WATS (WIDE AREA TELEPHONE SERVICE) but which applies to incoming calls.

IOCS *abbr.* Input/output control system.

irrational number Any of the numbers such as $\sqrt{2}$ which can be shown to exist and upon which the operations defined upon the rational numbers can be shown to be defined, but which cannot be expressed as a quotient of a pair of integers. For practical purposes, these numbers can be approximated by rational numbers to any degree of accuracy desired.

isochronous *adj.* Regularly periodic.

item *n.* A single unit or article included in a category, series, or enumeration.

iterate *v.* To execute (a process, series of instructions, operation, or the like) repeatedly.

iterative process Any method of computing a desired result in which the same sequence of operations is iterated, yielding a closer approximation of the correct value each time. Such a process may be continued until the computed result has the desired degree of precision.

ITS *abbr.* Invitation to send.

ITU *abbr.* INTERNATIONAL TELECOMMUNICATION UNION.

J

jack *n.* A connecting device provided with metal spring clips to which the wires of a circuit can be connected and into which a fitting plug can be inserted.

jam *n.* In a punch-card machine, a fault condition that inhibits or interferes with the normal movement of cards within the machine.

jitter *n.* Short-term instability of a signal or waveform, as resulting from fluctuations in supply voltages, components, etc.

job *n.* A set of tasks prescribed for execution by a computer, usually considered to include all necessary routines, linkages, files, and instructions to the operating system.

job control statement Any statement included in a job in order to identify it or describe its requirements to the operating system.

job library A concatenation of partitioned data sets identified by the user and serving as the principal source of load modules for a specified job.

job management The functions performed by the JOB SCHEDULER and MASTER SCHEDULER collectively.

job-oriented terminal In a communications system, a specialized terminal designed to handle data of a particular sort or designed to operate in a particular environment.

job scheduler A program function that controls input job streams and system output, allots input/output devices for jobs and job steps, attaches tasks corresponding to job steps, and in general regulates the use of a computer system by the jobs assigned to it.

job statement In an input job stream, a control statement that marks the beginning of a series of job control statements for a particular job.

job step A computer routine that is explicitly identified by a job control statement, one or more such routines comprising a single job.

jump *n.* Any departure from the execution of instructions in the order in which they occur in storage. See CONDITIONAL JUMP.

junk *n.* A garbled or otherwise unintelligible sequence of signals or other data, especially as received from a communications channel; hash; garbage.

justify *v.* To arrange or align (data, especially printed data) with respect to one or more reference lines or marks.

K

k *abbr.* KILO-.

Karnaugh map In logic, a rectangular diagram of a logic function, drawn in such a way that it contains a number of smaller rectangles, each of whose overlapping areas represents a unique combination of logic variables, every possible combination of variables being represented by such an intersection.

key *n.* One or more characters contained in a data item in order to identify it or control its use accessibility.

keyboard *n.* A device consisting of an array of levers each associated with a particular code element. Depressing any particular lever causes the associated code element to be selected or generated.

keyboard lockout An arrangement by which transmission from a particular keyboard is inhibited while other transmissions are taking place on the same circuit.

keyboard send/receive A teletypewriter TRANSCEIVER having transmission capability only from a keyboard.

key click A transient resulting from the opening or closing of a set of electrical contacts.

key-click filter An electrical network designed to attenuate the undesired frequency components of a KEY CLICK.

keying *n.* The formation of an electrical signal by modulating a carrier into discrete pulses, by varying amplitude, frequency, or phase between distinct conditions.

keying chirps Variations in the frequency of a continuous wave signal resulting from some instability in the oscillator when it is keyed.

keying wave In a telegraphic communication

system, the waveform that is generated while the information portions of code characters are being transmitted.

key pulse See PUSHBUTTON DIALING.

keypunch **1** *n.* A keyboard-operated device used to punch information into cards or tape. **2** *v.* To operate such a machine.

key-verify *v.* To check (the information punched into a card) by means of a VERIFIER.

keyword *n.* Any of the words in a document or the title thereof which are significant in that they reflect the information content of the document.

kilo- *prefix* **1** 10^3 times (a specified unit). **2** Loosely, in data processing, 2^{10} (decimal 1,024) times (a specified unit).

KSR *abbr.* KEYBOARD SEND/RECEIVE.

KWIC *abbr.* Keyword in context.

L

label *n.* One or more characters associated with or attached to an item of data for purposes of identification.

laced card A card that has been punched in such a way that it has a lacelike appearance, usually containing no information.

lag *n.* **1** The period of time that elapses between a pair of related events. **2** In a steady-state alternating-current circuit, the difference in phase measured between two points.

landline facilities Communications facilities within the continental United States that are controlled by domestic common carriers.

language *n.* Any set of symbols and the rules governing interrelations between the symbols, which can be used to convey or represent information.

language translator A routine, such as an assembler or compiler, designed to accept input statements in one language and produce equivalent output statements in another.

latency *n.* The time that elapses between the instant at which the decoding of an address is completed, and the instant at which the transfer of information from the addressed location actually begins.

leader *n.* On a reel of tape, a section at the beginning that is deliberately left blank.

leading edge Of a punched card, that edge which enters the machine first.

leapfrog test A routine that performs a checkout by copying itself throughout storage.

leg *n.* In a computer routine, the sequence of instructions that is followed between two branch points.

letter *n.* Any graphic, exclusive of diacritical or punctuation marks, which alone or in combination with other similar graphics is capable of representing one or more of the sound elements of a spoken language.

letters shift **1** A change of position of a teletypewriter carriage that allows alphabetic characters to be printed in proper sequence. **2** The control character that causes this change of position to occur.

level compensator In the receiving equipment of a telegraph circuit, a device that causes the output signal to remain fairly constant regardless of the strength of the signal received from the line.

LF *abbr.* The LINE FEED CHARACTER.

library *n.* An organized collection of information, as of input data, problem routines, subroutines, control routines, or the like.

library routine A routine which has been proved to be free of mistakes and is maintained in a library.

light pen A small penlike device that emits a thin beam of light that is capable of affecting the phosphors of a cathode-ray tube used in a display in such a way as to enter visual data into a computer.

light stability In optical character recognition, the degree to which an image resists change of color as a result of exposure to radiant energy.

light stylus A LIGHT PEN.

limit *n.* In mathematics, **1** A finite number related to a sequence S_n in such a way that there exists a number N for which $|L - S_n| < \epsilon$, when $n > N$, ϵ being an arbitrarily small positive number. Symbolically,

$$L = \lim_{x \to \infty} S_n.$$

2 A finite number L related to a function $f(x)$ in such a way that there exists a number δ for which $|L - f(x)| < \epsilon$, whenever $|x - a| < \delta$, ϵ being an arbitrarily small positive number. Symbolically,

$$L = \lim_{x \to a} f(x).$$

limited *adj.* Indicating a process whose speed is restricted most by a particular one of its component activities: used mostly in compounds: *tape-limited*; *input/output-limited*.

limit priority In a multitask operation, a specification associated with each task indicating the highest priority that it can assign to itself or any of its subtasks.

line adapter In IBM terminology, a MODEM that is a feature of a particular device.

linear *adj.* **1** Indicating an algebraic equation in which all of the variables are present in the first degree only, that is, an equation in which none of the variables are raised to powers other than unity or multiplied together. **2** Indicating a differential equation in which the dependent variable and any of its derivatives that appear are present in the first degree only.

linear optimization LINEAR PROGRAMMING.

linear programming The mathematical theory concerned with the maximization or minimization of a linear function some or all of whose variables are subject to a set of linear constraints, more explicitly, it is the extremization of the linear form $f(x_i) = \sum_{i=1}^{n} a_i x_i$, $x_i \geq 0$ subject to the set of linear constraints $\sum_{i=1}^{n} b_{ij} x_i = c_j$, $j = 1, 2, \ldots, m$.

line control LINE DISCIPLINE.

line discipline Any of various procedures designed to adjust the operating parameters of a transmission system to correct or optimum values.

line feed character A control character that causes the printing or display position to be advanced to the next line.

line hit Any electrical disturbance that causes spurious signals to be introduced into a communications system.

line level The ratio of the signal levels at two points on a transmission, generally expressed in decibels.

line load A measure of the use of a communications circuit during a specified period of time, usually expressed as a percentage of maximum circuit capability.

line loop The part of a telephone circuit that comprises a subscriber's telephone set and the pair of wires that connect it with the central office DISTRIBUTING FRAME.

line loop resistance The electrical resistance of a line loop.

line noise Electrical noise that originates on a transmission line.

line printer A device that prints an entire line of characters simultaneously. Compare CHARACTER PRINTER.

line relay A relay that is actuated by signals carried on a transmission line.

line speed The maximum rate at which information can be carried by a specified communications channel, expressed, generally in BAUDS or BITS per second.

line stretcher An impedance-matching device designed to operate in conjunction with coaxial transmission lines.

line switching A communications switching system that establishes contact between the sending and receiving units at the time of actual transmission. Compare MESSAGE SWITCHING; STEP-BY-STEP SWITCH.

link *n.* A COMMUNICATION LINK.

linkage *n.* In programming, a sequence of code that serves to connect a pair of independently coded routines.

linkage editor A program that produces a load module by transforming object modules into a format that is acceptable for fetching, combining separately generated object modules and previously processed load modules into a single load module, resolving symbolic cross references between them, replacing, deleting, and adding control sections automatically on request, and providing overlay facilities for modules requesting them.

linked subroutine A subroutine that is connected to the main routine by a LINKAGE.

link library A partitioned data set which is generally accessible and, unless otherwise specified, is available for use in fetching load modules specified by execute statements and attach, link, load, and transfer control macro instructions.

list 1 *n.* A set of items arranged in some particular order. **2** *v.* To arrange (a set of items) in a list. **3** *v.* To print (every item of input data) that is relevant with respect to some criterion.

list processing A method of processing in which the data is arranged in lists, CHAINED LISTS being most often used so that the effective order of items can be varied independently of their physical locations.

literal *n.* In a source program, a symbol or quantity that, rather than referring to data, is itself data.

literature search A systematic and exhaustive search for and of published material that pertains to a specified topic, including, in general, the preparation of abstracts of that material.

load *v.* **1** To introduce (data, programs, or the like) into storage or registers. **2** To introduce lumped inductance into a transmission to minimize distortion.

load-and-go A technique in which the loading of a program, such assembly or compilation as may be necessary, and its execution proceed without interruption.

load mode In certain variable-word-length computers, a mode of data transmission such that some delimiters travel with the data.

load module **1** The output of a LINKAGE EDITOR. **2** A program whose format is such that it can be loaded into main storage for execution.

local central office A central office equipped to terminate subscriber lines and establish connection with other central offices.

local channel In private line services, the part of an intraexchange through a channel that is designed to connect the main station with an interexchange channel.

local loop A channel that serves to connect subscriber equipment to the terminating equipment in the central office exchange.

local service area The area that contains all the telephone stations that a customer paying a flat rate is permitted to call free of toll charges.

location *n.* Loosely and in general, an identifiable place in which data is or can be stored.

locking *adj.* Indicating any of various code-extension characters that apply to an unspecified number of succeeding characters. Compare NON-LOCKING.

lockout **1** *n.* In a telephone circuit containing an echo-suppressor, the suppression of signals originating at either or both subscriber stations, either as a result of a high level of local circuit noise or as a result of continuous speech by one or the other subscriber. **2** *v.* To render (unaddressed terminals on a multipoint line) incapable of receiving transmitted data.

log *n. informal* A LOGARITHM.

logarithm *n.* A number m related to another number p by

$$B^m = p,$$

where B is an arbitrarily chosen number larger than 1. Usually m is written $\log_B p$. Logarithms have the basic properties that

$$\log pq = \log p + \log q$$

and

$$\log p^q = q \log p.$$

In the systems most often used $B = 10$ (common logarithms) or $B = e = 2.71828 \ldots$ (natural logarithms). The common logarithm of p is written $\log_{10} p$ or simply $\log p$; the natural logarithm of p is written $\log_e p$ or $\ln p$. **— logarithmic** *adj.*

logger *n.* An automatic device that records the dynamic variables of physical processes with respect to time.

logic *n.* **1** FORMAL LOGIC. **2** SYMBOLIC LOGIC.

logical add The logic operator OR (which see).

logical file A set that is composed of one or more logical records.

logical multiply The logic operator AND (which see).

logical record A collection of data items which are not necessarily stored in the same physical record or even in the same physical medium.

logic circuit Any of various switching circuits, as AND-gates, OR-gates, etc., that can perform LOGIC OPERATIONS or represent LOGIC FUNCTIONS.

logic design The working relations between the

elements of a data-processing system, generally expressed in some form of symbolic logic, independent of the particular hardware used.

logic diagram A diagram that expresses a particular logic design and, sometimes, the hardware employed.

logic element In general, any device that is capable of executing a LOGIC FUNCTION or LOGIC OPERATOR.

logic function An expression that includes one or a combination of LOGIC OPERATORS.

logic instruction An instruction that causes a LOGIC OPERATION to be executed.

logic operator Any of the operators AND, OR, NOR, etc.

logic shift A shift operation in which data is moved through all available positions with, in particular, no positions reserved for SIGN BITS.

logic symbol A symbol used to represent either a LOGIC ELEMENT or a LOGIC OPERATOR.

longitudinal redundancy check A system of error control based on the arrangement of data in blocks according to some preset rule, the correctness of each character within the block being determined on the basis of the rule.

longitudinal redundancy check character On a magnetic tape using non-return-to-zero indication and on which a character is represented by a lateral row of bits, a character placed at the end of each block for the purpose of checking the parity of each track in the block longitudinally and for restoring each of the tracks to the dc erase polarity.

long lines In the Bell System, a department of AT&T that provides the majority of the intercompany transmission facilities.

look-up TABLE LOOK-UP.

loop *n.* **1** A sequence of instructions that is iterated until some condition is satisfied. **2** A magnetic hysteresis loop. **3** A closed path through which an electric current can flow.

loopback test A checkout procedure in which signals are routed from a test center through a data set or loopback switch and returned to the test center for evaluation.

loop jack switchboard A patch panel provided with rows of jacks that allow physical access to local loops, the maximum capacity of such an installation being 90 channels. Each column of four jacks contains a pair of looping jacks, a set jack, and a miscellaneous jack and is designed to access one LOCAL LOOP.

loss *n.* In communications, a decrease in signal power as measured between two points.

low-order *adj.* Indicating that digit of a number which has the least significance.

low-order position In most systems of numerical notation, the position furthest to the right.

low speed In general, a data transmission rate that is less than or equal to 600 bits per second.

low tape In a paper tape perforating unit, an indication that the supply of tape is nearly exhausted.

LP *abbr.* LINEAR PROGRAMMING.

LPM *abbr.* Lines per minute.

LRC *abbr.* The LONGITUDINAL REDUNDANCY CHECK CHARACTER.

LTRS *abbr.* LETTERS SHIFT.

Lukasiewicz notation PREFIX NOTATION.

lumped *adj.* Indicating elements of electrical impedance that are concentrated in discrete units rather than being distributed over a transmission line or through space.

lumped loading The modification of the electrical characteristics of a transmission line by the insertion of lumped impedances, generally inductances, at regular intervals.

M

machine *n.* Any item of hardware used in data processing, in particular, the central processing unit of a computer and, often, the units under its direct control.

machine address An ABSOLUTE ADDRESS.

machine code An OPERATION CODE that is directly useable by a machine.

machine-independent Indicating procedures, programs, etc., whose functioning is substantially the same regardless of the machine on which they are executed.

machine instruction An instruction that can be directly decoded and executed by a machine.

machine language A LANGUAGE that can be directly interpreted by a machine, in particular, the language, peculiar in general to each machine, in which MACHINE INSTRUCTIONS are expressed.

machine learning The ability of an artificial system to improve its execution of a task on the basis of information gained from prior executions or attempts at executions of the same task or closely related tasks. See ARTIFICIAL INTELLIGENCE.

machine-readable medium A medium from which a given sensing device can extract data.

machine run The execution of one or more machine routines that are joined by appropriate linkages to form an operational unit.

machine-sensible information Information that is in a form such that it can be accepted by a specified machine.

machine word A COMPUTER WORD.

macroelement *n.* An ordered set of data elements that are treated as a unit and provided with a single data use identifier.

macroinstruction *n.* In a source language or programming language, a single instruction that causes a specific sequence of instruction to be generated in the object language program.

macroprogramming *n.* Programming in which MACROINSTRUCTIONS are exclusively or extensively used.

magazine *n.* An INPUT MAGAZINE.

magnetic card A card having a surface of magnetic material which can, by appropriate magnetization of selected areas, be used to store data.

magnetic core A piece of magnetic material that has a high permeability and, often, a high retentivity as well. It may be placed inside of a current-carrying coil to intensify the magnetic field, or it may be placed in close conjunction with a current-carrying conductor to retain magnetism after the current has ceased to flow. In the latter configuration, it is as a storage or logic element in computers.

magnetic delay line A DELAY LINE whose operation depends on the propagation time of magnetic impulses.

magnetic disc An information-storage device consisting of a rapidly rotating plane circular surface that is selectively magnetized in various portions.

magnetic disk A magnetic disc.

magnetic drum An information-storage device similar to a magnetic disc except that the rotating surface used is a right circular cylinder.

magnetic head A specially designed electromagnet that can be energized by a time-varying current and used for introducing information into magnetic discs, drums, or tapes and extracting or erasing it.

magnetic hysteresis loop A closed curve that indicates the HYSTERESIS in the relation between magnetizing force and magnetic induction in a magnetic material.

magnetic induction A vector associated with the mechanical force exerted on a current-carrying conductor that is located in a magnetic field.

magnetic ink An ink in which particles of a magnetic material are suspended and which activates appropriate sensors.

magnetic ink character recognition The acceptance by a machine of information in the form of characters printed in magnetic ink.

magnetic storage Any form of storage device whose operation depends on the properties of a magnetic material.

magnetic tape A thin ribbon of plastic or other material coated with a magnetic substance capable of retaining signals fed onto it.

magnetic thin film A THIN FILM having magnetic properties, often useful in logic and storage devices.

magnitude n. The size of a number when its algebraic sign is disregarded; ABSOLUTE VALUE.

main distributing frame 1 A distributing frame that serves to associate any outside line entering a central office with any terminal of any subscriber multiple line or with any other outside line. 2 In a private exchange, a distributing frame serving an analogous purpose.

main frame The basic or essential portion of an assembly of hardware, in particular, the CENTRAL PROCESSING UNIT of a computer.

main path The principal branch of a routine taken by a computer in the course of its execution.

main station 1 A telephone station that is designated by a distinct call number and directly connected to a central office. 2 In leased lines for customer equipment, the main interface between such equipment and the local loop.

main storage In a computer, the general purpose storage that has the shortest ACCESS TIME.

maintenance n. 1 Any activity designed to keep a system, including hardware and software, in proper operating condition. 2 FILE MAINTENANCE.

maintenance time The time required for performance of maintenance on hardware.

major cycle 1 In a recirculating serial storage device, the maximum access time. 2 A number of minor cycles.

majority n. A logic operator having the property that if X is a statement and $P_1, P_2, \ldots P_n$ are statements and X is defined as equivalent to the majority of $P_1, P_2, \ldots P_n$, then X is true whenever more than half of $P_1, P_2, \ldots P_n$ are true.

majority gate An item of hardware that implements the MAJORITY logic operator.

major total The total that results when a summation is terminated by the most significant change of group.

makeup time The fraction of available time consumed in reruns that are made necessary by malfunctions or mistakes that occurred during previous operating time.

malfunction n. Any incorrect functioning of a system as a result of a fault in an item of hardware.

management information systems Management in which automatic data processing is used.

mantissa n. **1** In computer arithmetic, the part of a FLOATING-POINT NUMBER that does not represent an exponent, that is, the multiplier that is applied to the base raised to a specified power. **2** The fractional part of a logarithm to the base 10.

manual exchange An EXCHANGE in which the intervention of a human operator is necessary in order for a call to be completed.

manual input 1 The use of a manually operated device to enter data into a machine at the time of processing. **2** The data so entered.

manual operation The processing of data in a system composed of devices that are operated by hand.

map v. To indicate or establish a relation between the members of two sets A and B such that for each element a of the set A there corresponds a unique element a' of the set B.

marginal check A preventative maintenance procedure in which various operating parameters are deliberately varied from their nominal values to the extremes of their tolerances in order to expose latent or incipient defects.

margin control A RANGE FINDER.

margin-punched card A card on which punching is limited to the perimeter, the remaining space being reserved for printed or written data.

mark n. **1** A current, voltage, or other signal condition that is interpreted as a binary 1. Compare SPACE. **2** A FLAG. **3** A GROUP MARK.

mark-hold The transmission of a steady MARK as the normal indication of a no-traffic line condition, sometimes a customer-selected option.

Markov chain In probability theory, a sequence of events such that the probability of each event depends only on the condition that prevails just prior to its occurrence and not on the way in which that condition arose.

mark-sense To indicate a position on a card by means of a pencil that leaves an electrically conductive mark, conversion to machine punching following at a later time.

mark-to-space transition The transition or switching from a MARK to a SPACE.

mask n. **1** A pattern according to which some characters from a larger pattern are selected and others rejected. **2** A filter.

mass storage 1 A storage having a large capacity. **2** A large-capacity storage whose contents are readily accessible to the central processing unit of a computer.

master card A card, usually the first of the group with which it is associated, that contains information about a group of cards.

master clock The principal source of the timing pulses that control the internal cycles of a computer.

master file A file that either is maintained for a relatively long time, is infrequently changed, or s used as the authoritative source of data in the performance of a particular job.

master scheduler The control program function that allows an operator to initiate actions, cause requested information to be delivered, and, thus, override the normal control functions of the system.

master station On a multipoint circuit, a unit that controls all other units for purposes of polling, selection, or both.

match v. To carry out a comparison of (a pair of data items) in order to establish that they are identical.

mathematical check A programmed checking procedure that verifies that the defined mathematical properties of various operations hold, that is, for instance, a check that verifies that a sum is independent of the order in which a pair of numbers is added.

mathematical model A set of equations, constraints, and the like that describe or represent some process of interest in the real world.

mathematical programming In operations research, any of various procedures for determining the value or values of the INDEPENDENT VARIABLE or variables for which a function subject to constraints has maxima or minima.

mathematical subroutine A subroutine whose output is related to the argument supplied to it by a well-defined mathematical function, as the sine, cosine, exponential or the like.

matrix n. **1** A rectangular array of numbers X_{ij}, where the subscripts i, j indicate respectively the row and column in which each X is located. A matrix in which $i_{max} = r$ and $j_{max} = s$ is called an r by s ($r \times s$) matrix. **2** An analogous array of numbers $X_{ij...n}$, in n dimensions. **3** A network, normally acting as an encoder or decoder, in which a set of input signals is transformed to a different set of output signals.

matrix storage Storage in which the location of each element is defined by at least two coordinates.

maximum n. The value of a function $f(x)$ at a point x_0 where $f(x_0)$ is algebraically the largest value of $f(x)$ in some interval about x_0. If the derivatives $f'(x)$ and $f''(x)$ exist at x_0 and $f'(x_0) = 0$, $f''(x_0) < 0$, the function $f(x)$ has a maximum at x_0.

maximum-effort control system A FEEDBACK CONTROL SYSTEM which is nonlinear in that the compensating device operates either full "on" or full "off." Systems of this type appear to have advantages in speed of response over linear systems.

maxterm n. A Boolean sum of n variables, each variable being present in either its true or complemented form. See also MINTERM.

MDF abbr. MAIN DISTRIBUTING FRAME.

mean n. See AVERAGE; GEOMETRIC MEAN.

mean time between failures A figure of merit for the reliability of a system, calculated on a statistical basis from known failure rates of its various components, generally on the assumption that the failure of a single component causes failure of the entire system.

measure *n.* In set theory, that property of a set that denotes how many objects there are in it.

medium *n.* Any physical means that can be used to store data, as, for instance, cards or paper or magnetic tape.

medium speed In data transmission, a speed bounded by 600 bits per second and the upper limit of a voice-grade channel.

mega- *prefix* One million, 10^6, times a specified unit.

memory *n.* STORAGE.

memory fill STORAGE FILL.

memory protection STORAGE PROTECTION.

mercury storage A type of storage that consists of a recirculating acoustic delay line in which mercury is the medium through which the pulses are transmitted.

mercury-wetted relay A type of relay in which mercury acts as the conductive medium that makes and breaks contact.

merge *v.* To form one set of items from (two or more such sets) with, in general, some sequence of combination implied or specified.

mesh *v.* To MERGE.

message *n.* A unit of information, generally arbitrary in length, whose boundaries are either implied or specifically defined.

message circuit A long-distance telephone circuit whose use is available to the public, as opposed to a circuit of this type that is reserved for private use.

message heading A HEADER.

message routing The selection of an appropriate circuit path for a message.

message switching A technique in which a message is received and stored until the proper outgoing circuit is available, at which time it is retransmitted.

MICR *abbr.* MAGNETIC INK CHARACTER RECOGNITION.

micro- *prefix* $10^{-6} \times$ a specified unit.

microcircuit *n.* An electronic circuit composed of elements that are fabricated and interconnected in such a way as to render them inseparable and the total package very small. See INTEGRATED CIRCUIT.

microcode *n.* Code that makes use of microinstructions, not normally used in programming.

microinstruction *n.* An instruction that causes a single, basic machine operation to be performed. The normal instruction repertoire uses microinstructions in combinations, and they are not usually accessible to the programmer.

microprogramming *n.* Programming in which MICROINSTRUCTIONS are directly used.

microsecond *n.* A millionth of a second; 10^{-6} second.

microwave *n.* An electromagnetic wave whose frequency lies in the range approximately bounded by 1,000 Mhz and 300,000 Mhz.

millisecond *n.* A thousandth of a second; 10^{-3} second.

minimum *n.* The value of a function $f(x)$ at a point x_0 where $f(x_0)$ is algebraically the smallest value of $f(x)$ in some interval about x_0. If the derivatives $f'(x)$ and $f''(x)$ exist at x_0 and $f'(x) = 0$, $f''(x) > 0$, the function $f(x)$ has a minimum at x_0.

minimum-distance code A binary code in which any pair of characters is separated by a specified minimum SIGNAL DISTANCE.

minor cycle In a storage device that allows serial access to storage positions, the time that elapses between the appearance of corresponding parts of successive words.

minor total The total that results when a summation is terminated by the least significant change of group.

minterm *n.* A Boolean product of *n* variables, each variable being present in either its true or complemented form. There is in Boolean algebra a pair of theorems that guarantee that any Boolean function of *n* variables can be expressed as a sum of a set of minterms or a product of a set of MAXTERMS.

minuend *n.* A number from which another number is, or is to be, subtracted.

minus *adj.* A word indicating that the number immediately following is negative.

minus sign A symbol (—) used to express minus, for example given a number k, where $k > 0$, by definition $-k < 0$, and $|-k| = k$.

miscellaneous intercept In telegraph message-switching systems leased from the Bell System; **1** the interception of a single-address message that contains a nonvalid call-directing code, and/or **2** the interception of a multiple-address message without a valid multiple-address code.

mistake *n.* In general, any action on the part of a human being that produces a result that is unintended or useless.

mixed radix Indicating a system of numeration, as, for example, the biquinary system (see BIQUINARY CODE), in which more than one RADIX is used.

mixed radix notation A form of positional representation in which the ratios of the significances of adjacent digit positions are integers with at least one of them being different from the others.

mnemonic *n.* A mnemonic symbol.

mnemonic symbol A symbol designed in such a way as to be easily remembered by human beings, as, for example, A for add or MPY for multiply.

mod/demod. *abbr.* MODULATOR-DEMODULATOR.

mode *n.* **1** Any particular method or manner of operation, as for example, the binary mode, alphameric mode, numeric mode, or the like. **2** In statistics, the most common or frequent value of a variable, as, for example, the one grade received by more students (of a defined group) than any other. **3** An ACCESS MODE.

model *n.* A MATHEMATICAL MODEL.

modem *n.* A MODULATOR-DEMODULATOR.

modular *adj.* Of, having to do with, or constructed from modules.

modulate *v.* To vary some characteristic of (an electromagnetic wave; electric current, etc.), generally in order to impress on it information that is to be transmitted. Assuming, for example, a sinusoidal carrier of the form

$$C(t) = A \cos (\omega t + \phi),$$

modulation could be accomplished by varying A, ω, or ϕ, or several of these at once, in accordance with some modulating function. — **modulator** *n.* — **modulation** *n.*

modulator-demodulator Any of various devices that perform modulation and demodulation for signals transmitted via communications facilities.

module *n.* **1** A program unit that is separate and distinctly identifiable with respect to operations such as compilation, assembly, loading, and combination with other such units. **2** A complete and discretely packaged subassembly of a larger system.

modulo N See RING OF INTEGERS MODULO *N*.

modulo N check A RESIDUE CHECK.

monadic Boolean operator A Boolean operator, as, for example NOT, that can apply to only one operand or its equivalent.

monadic operation An operation that can apply to just one operand or its equivalent.

monitor *n.* 1 A software or hardware subsystem that senses certain or all of the operating parameters of a larger system for purposes of supervision, control, verification, or the like. 2 *v.* To perform the actions or functions of a monitor in relation to (a system or process).

monitor printer A device that produces a printout of any message transmitted over the circuit to which it is connected.

monolithic integrated circuit An integrated circuit in which all components are formed on the same substrate of semiconductor material.

monostable *n.* Indicating a device that has at least two states and is stable in one and only one of them.

Monte Carlo method The use of random sampling techniques in deriving estimated probable solutions to mathematical problems, generally used when the problem is otherwise intractable.

move *v.* TRANSMIT.

move mode In certain variable-word-length computers, a mode of operation in which data can be transmitted without certain delimiters being transmitted as well.

M response A V RESPONSE.

MTBF *abbr.* MEAN TIME BETWEEN FAILURES.

multiaddress *adj.* Indicating an instruction format in which there is more than a single address part.

multidrop line A communications line or circuit by means of which several stations are interconnected.

multijob operation The concurrent execution of job steps from two or more jobs.

multilevel address An INDIRECT ADDRESS.

multiple-address message A message that is to be delivered to two or more destinations.

multiple-aperture core A magnetic core that contains two or more holes through which wires that can carry electrical impulses can pass and which, thus, contain two or more closed paths for magnetic flux. Cores of this type allow nondestructive READ operations to be performed.

multiple punching On a card, the punching of two or more holes in a single column by means of more than a single keystroke.

multiplex 1 *n.* The operation of a communications channel in such a way that elements of two or more signals or messages are rapidly interleaved or transmitted simultaneously. 2 *v.* To transmit (two or more messages or signals) in effect simultaneously by means of such operation. See FREQUENCY DIVISION MULTIPLEX; TIME DIVISION MULTIPLEX.

multiplexer channel A channel that, operating by means of time-division multiplex, is able to control and communicate with a number of input/output units concurrently.

multiplexor channel A MULTIPLEXER CHANNEL.

multiplicand *n.* A number multiplied, or to be multiplied, by another.

multiplication *n.* The determination of a number *c* that is equal to *a* taken *b* many times, all added together.

multiplier *n.* A number by which another number is, or is to be multiplied.

multiply *v.* To perform multiplication.

multipoint line A MULTIDROP LINE.

multiprocessing *n.* The simultaneous execution of two or more instruction sequences, as by means of a multiprocessor.

multiprocessor *n.* An automatic data-processing system that contains two or more processing units under integrated control, having, thus, the capability of executing two or more computer programs simultaneously.

multiprogramming *n.* A technique by means of which a single computer can be used to perform concurrent execution of two or more programs.

multipunch *n.* MULTIPLE PUNCHING.

multistation *adj.* Indicating a network in which each of the stations has the capability of communicating with the others.

Mylar *n.* A polyester film often used as a base for magnetic tapes, perforated tapes, or other similar information media: a trademark of DuPont.

N

n *symbol* An arbitrary or unspecified real number that may be restricted to integral or rational values either by definition or context.

NAK *abbr.* The NEGATIVE ACKNOWLEDGE CHARACTER.

NAND *n.* A logic operator equivalent to NOT AND, that is, if X and $P_1, P_2, \ldots P_n$, are statements and X is equivalent to NAND $P_1, P_2, \ldots P_n$, then X is true if and only if one of the statements $P_1, P_2, \ldots P_n$ is false.

NAND gate A hardware module that implements the operator NAND.

nano- *prefix* 10^{-9} times a specified unit.

nanosecond *n.* One billionth of a second; 10^{-9} second.

natural language A language, as any of the spoken and written languages in general use, whose contents and syntax reflect and describe a consensus of current usage rather than a set of rigidly prescribed rules.

natural logarithm See LOGARITHM.

Truth table for
NAND operator

A	B	$(A \cdot B)'$ *
0	0	1
0	1	1
1	0	1
1	1	0

* Symbolic notation for A **NAND** B, equivalent to NOT (A AND B)

n-core-per-bit storage A storage device in which each bit to be stored requires the use of *n* cores.

near-end crosstalk Crosstalk that propagates through the channel that it disturbs in a direction opposite to the direction of signal propagation in the channel from which the disturbance arises, the terminal of the disturbed channel at which the interference is greatest ordinarily being in rather close proximity to the energized terminal of the channel in which the disturbance arises.

needle *n.* A slender rod or probe that may be passed through each of a set of cards that has in any one punching position either a hole or a notch, a selection or sorting operation being performed as the notched cards fall free of the probe and the others remain attached.

negation *n.* The execution of the logic operator NOT.

negative acknowledge character A communication control character (or sometimes an accuracy control character) transmitted by a receiver back to a sender as a negative response.

negative feedback See FEEDBACK.

neper *n.* A unit whose characteristics and derivation are similar to those of the DECIBEL except that it is based on the natural LOGARITHMS rather than on the common logarithms.

nest *v.* To include (subroutines) in subroutines or (data) in data in such a way that they act or are contained at different levels of hierarchy and can be recursively executed or accessed.

network *n.* **1** A system composed of a set of interconnected points, in particular; **a** a set of stations interconnected by communications channels, or **b** a set of interconnected electrical components. **2** A COMPUTER NETWORK.

network analog An electrical network whose variables are related in a manner analogous to those of a system or mathematical problem under study, often used as an aid in the solution or analysis of such a system or problem.

network analyzer A device designed to simulate any of various electrical networks.

neutral transmission A method of signal transmission in which a MARK is represented by the presence of a current on a line and a SPACE is represented by a no current condition. Compare POLAR TRANSMISSION.

neutral zone An area or interval of time within which a system is not in the condition which all necessary action has been taken to put it in, as for example, the time that a flip-flop requires to change states after the reception of a pulse.

new line character A control character that causes the printing or display position to advance to the beginning of the next line.

nibble *n.* In programmer slang, a portion of a BYTE.

nines complement In the decimal numeration system, the radix-minus-one COMPLEMENT.

NL *abbr.* The NEW LINE CHARACTER.

n-level address A multilevel address in which *n* levels of addressing are specified.

node *n.* In the graphic representation of information, processes, or the like, a point that symbolizes a condition or an event.

noise *n.* **1** Any disturbance that interferes with the functioning of a system, especially a random fluctuation of one of the variables of the system, such as voltage or current. **2** A randomly generated signal whose characteristics can be specified to some extent by means of a statistical distribution.

noise generator A system designed to generate noise, in particular, a routine that generates random numbers for use in the simulation of analog noise.

noise killer An electrical network inserted into a telegraph circuit, usually at the sending end, in order to minimize undesirable interaction with other communications circuits.

noisy mode In floating-point arithmetic, a technique in which 1's rather than 0's are inserted into the low order position of the mantissa during left shifts associated with normalization, generally used to determine the sensitivity of a routine to truncation errors.

nominal speed The maximum rate at which a data transmission system or some component thereof can handle data, there being no allowance made for such functions as checking, tabbing, or the like, which lower the effective rate.

non-data set clocking A time base oscillator by means of which a business machine regulates the rate at which it transmits bits. See DATA SET CLOCKING.

nondestructive read A READ operation in which the stored data is not erased.

nonequivalence element A logic element that implements the operator EXCLUSIVE OR; an EXCLUSIVE OR gate.

nonerasable storage Fixed storage.

nonlinear *adj.* Not LINEAR.

nonlinear optimization Nonlinear programming.

nonlinear programming The mathematical theory concerned with the maximization or minimization of a function that is subject to certain constraints on the behavior of its variables where either the function itself or at least one of the constraints is nonlinear. Compare LINEAR PROGRAMMING.

nonloaded lines Transmission lines or cable pairs that have not been loaded with lumped inductances. See LOADING.

nonlocking *adj.* Indicating any of various code extension characters that apply to and change the interpretation of just a specified number of characters. Compare LOCKING.

non-polarized return-to-zero recording A RETURN-TO-REFERENCE RECORDING technique in which the reference condition (the condition that indicates spaces or 0's) is the absence of magnetization, marks or 1's being indicated by magnetization of a specified level and polarity.

non-return-to-reference recording NON-RETURN-TO-ZERO RECORDING.

non-return-to-zero "change" recording A method of recording in which 0's and 1's are represented by two specified different conditions of magnetization.

non-return-to-zero "mark" recording A recording technique in which a change on the condition of magnetization represents a 1, the absence of such a change indicating a 0.

non-return-to-zero recording A recording technique in which the reference condition is provided by a change between the states of magnetization representing 0 and 1.

nonsimultaneous transmission In general, transmission in which the system used can send data in only one direction at any given time.

nonvolatile storage A storage medium in which the retention of the stored information does not depend on any flow of energy.

NO OP A computer instruction that causes the machine to perform no operation except to advance to the next instruction in sequence.

NOR A logic operator equivalent to NOT OR, that is, if X and P_1, P_2, ... P_n, are statements and X is equivalent to NOR of P_1, P_2, ... P_n, then X is true if and only if all of the individual statements P_i are false.

Truth table for
NOR operator

A	B	$(A + B)'$*
0	0	1
1	0	0
0	1	0
1	1	0

* Symbolic notation for A **NOR** B, equivalent to NOT (A OR B)

NOR gate A hardware module that implements the operator NOR.

normal direction flow On a flowchart, a flow that proceeds from left to right or from top to bottom.

normalize v. **1** To adjust the characteristic and mantissa of (a floating-point number) in such a way that the mantissa lies within a specified range. **2** To put a set of numbers or mathematical symbols in some standard form.

normalized form The form taken by a floating-point number that has been adjusted so that its mantissa lies in a specified range.

NOT A logic operator having the property that if X and P are statements and X is equivalent to NOT P, then X is true if and only if P is false.

NOT AND See NAND.

notation n. Any system that is capable of representing information in nonvolatile form by means of symbols, characters, and positional relationships.

NOT gate A hardware module that implements the operator NOT.

NOT if-then See EXCLUSION.

NOT OR See NOR.

NRZ C abbr. NON-RETURN-TO-ZERO "CHANGE" RECORDING.

NRZ M abbr. NON-RETURN-TO-ZERO "MARK" RECORDING.

nucleus n. **1** The part of the control program that must always be in main storage. **2** The area of main storage used by the nucleus and transient control routines.

NUL abbr. The null character.

null character A control character used to fill unused time in a data-transmission system or space in a storage medium. While null characters may be inserted into or deleted from a character sequence at will with no change in meaning, it is possible that equipment control or data format will be affected.

null set In logic and set theory, a set that contains no members; the empty set.

null string A STRING whose members are identical with the NULL SET, that is, a string that contains no entities.

number 1 *n.* Any of a set of mathematical entities having certain defined properties and relationships between themselves, useful, in general, for the precise delineation of concepts such as quantity, position, degree, and the like. 2 *v.* To count or assign numbers to (physical or abstract entities).

numbering plan A telephone numbering system wherein each central office has a unique designation whose form is similar to that of all other central offices connected to the nationwide dialing network. The basic format is of ten dialed digits, the first three being an area code, the next three being an office code, and the final four being a station number.

number representation system A NUMERATION SYSTEM.

number system In loose usage, a numeration system.

numeral *n.* Any of a set of symbols by means of which numbers can be notated.

numeral system A NUMERATION SYSTEM.

numeration system Any conventionalized set of symbols and rules for their association by means of which numbers can be represented.

numerator *n.* In a fraction, the number that is understood to be divided by the other.

numeric *adj.* Of, having to do with, or represented by numerals.

numerical *adj.* Composed of or having to do with numbers.

numerical analysis The study of methods for obtaining approximate solutions for mathematical problems that appear in their generalized forms to be insoluble. Solution by such methods generally requires that all quantities be expressed as their actual values and that an exceedingly large number of arithmetic operations be carried out. In this the computer is almost an indispensable tool. An example of the technique may be in order. Suppose one had to solve the differential equation $dy/dx = ky$ (a simple equation, to be sure, and one that is soluble by ordinary means). If we use the definition

$$dy/dx = \lim_{h \to 0} \frac{f(x+h) - f(x)}{h},$$

we can write

$$\frac{f(x+h) - f(x)}{kh} \cong y \text{ for small } h.$$

In order to proceed we need to know an x, y pair that will satisfy the solution. This information known as an initial condition or boundary condition, would be needed to evaluate the general solution in any case. For the example let 0, 1 be the x, y solution pair, let k be 3, and we arbitrarily choose $h = .1$. Thus if we set $y = f(x)$ we have

$$\frac{f(.1) - 1}{.3} = 1.$$

Solving for $f(.1)$ we get $f(.1) = 1.3$. Note that this generates another x, y pair that can be used in iterating the process, yielding finally a table of values for x and y that will, if h is chosen small enough, closely approximate the function $y = e^{3x}$, which is in fact the true solution for the given initial conditions. The usefulness of a computer in obtaining a very accurate solution to even this simple problem should be obvious.

numerical control Automatic control of a process in real time by a device that uses numerical data, by means of sensing and control devices in contact with the process and analog-to-digital and digital-to-analog converters as needed.

numeric character A DIGIT.

numeric code A code using a code set that contains digits and associated special characters exclusively.

numeric data Data that is represented exclusively by numerals and special characters.

numeric data code A NUMERIC CODE designed for data.

numeric word A word composed exclusively of characters from a NUMERIC CODE.

Nyquist interval The interval of time occupied by each code element when a communications channel is being used at the NYQUIST RATE.

Nyquist rate The maximum rate N at which code elements can be resolved without ambiguity in a communications channel of a certain limited bandwidth in which the peak noise level is less than one-half the quantum step between code signals, given by

$$N = 2B,$$

where B is the bandwidth of the channel in hertz.

O

object code Code that is expressed in OBJECT LANGUAGE, as after compilation or assembly.

objective function In operations research, the function to be maximized or minimized in a given problem.

object language The language used by a COMPILER or ASSEMBLER for its output.

object module A module that is output with respect to a compiler or assembler and input with respect to a linkage editor.

object program A program that has been completely compiled or assembled and is ready for loading.

object time The occasion on which an object language program is actually executed.

OCR *abbr.* OPTICAL CHARACTER RECOGNITION.

octal *adj.* **1** Of or having to do with a situation, characteristic, condition, or the like, in which there are eight distinct possibilities. **2** Indicating a system of numeration in which the radix is eight.

octal digit Any of the digits 1, 2, 3, 4, 5, 6, 7, 0, used in expressing numbers to the radix 8 (written 10 in octal form).

octet *n.* A BYTE that contains eight BITS.

octonary *adj.* OCTAL (def. 2).

odd-even check A PARITY CHECK.

off-hook In reference to a telephone or a data set that automatically accepts calls from a public switched system, activated; in use.

offline *adj.* Of or indicating such items of peripheral hardware as are not under the direct control of the central processing unit.

offline system In teleprocessing, a system that requires human intervention between the original recording functions and the ultimate data processing function, such intervention being necessary in conversion functions as well as in the loading and unloading operations associated with the use of point-to-point or data-gathering systems.

off-punch A punch that is improperly positioned in a column of a card.

offset *n.* In a control system, the difference between the desired value of the output variable and the value actually obtained when the system is operating in a steady state.

offset stacker A card stacker that can, under machine control, stack certain cards so that they protrude from the deck in such a way as to allow physical identification.

on-demand system A system that provides information or service at the time when it is requested.

one-address SINGLE-ADDRESS.

one-for-one Of, related to, or indicating an assembly routine in which one source language instruction is converted to one object language instruction.

one-level address A DIRECT ADDRESS.

one-plus-one address Indicating an instruction in which there is contained an operand address and an address that gives the location of the next instruction.

ones complement In the binary numeration system, the radix-minus-one COMPLEMENT.

one-to-one Indicating a mapping between two sets *A* and *B* such that if *A* is the source set and *B* the target set every element of *B* has a corresponding element in *A* and every element that is distinct in *A* has a distinct image in *B*.

one-way-trunk A trunk connecting central offices between which traffic can originate at one end only.

on-hook Deactivated; not in use. See OFF-HOOK.

online *adj.* Of or indicating peripheral hardware that is under direct control of the central processing unit.

online mass storage MASS STORAGE def. 2.

online system 1 In teleprocessing, a system in which input data enters the computer directly from the point of origin and/or output data is transmitted directly to the point of use. **2** Indicating a data communication system in which the computer transmits directly into a telegraph line.

op code An OPERATION CODE.

openended *adj.* Indicating a process, system, or the like to which additions can be made.

open-loop control system A control system in which the output variable is directly controlled by the system input, there being no FEEDBACK.

open shop 1 Indicating a computer installation in which most of the programming is the responsibility of the problem originators rather than of specialists. **2** Indicating a computer installation in which most of the actual machine operation is carried on by user-programmers rather than by full-time trained operators.

open subroutine A subroutine that must be inserted into the main routine at each point where it is to be used, being subject to relocation as necessary.

open wire Any of a set of wires that are separated from each other and/or ground principally by air, solid insulators separating or supporting them at intervals.

open-wire line A transmission line composed principally of open wire.

operand *n.* A quantity, data field, or the like that is or is to be subjected to some arithmetic, logical, or other operation, generally identified in an instruction by an address.

operating ratio The ratio of OPERATING TIME to the total time of scheduled operation for a particular computer or system.

operating system A fairly complex computer routine that controls the execution of problem routines, often providing such services as scheduling, input/output control, debugging, compilation, data and storage management, and the like.

operating time The part of available time during which the hardware is operating and yielding results for which there is a high confidence level of correctness. This includes DEVELOPMENT TIME, PRODUCTION TIME, and MAKEUP TIME. Compare IDLE TIME.

operation *n.* Any defined action, in particular, the producing of a result by acting on one or more operands according to some rule such that the result is defined completely for any combination of operands not considered invalid according to that rule.

operational amplifier A high-gain feedback amplifier used as the basic unit of the analog computer and having its main application in function generation. The most usual config-

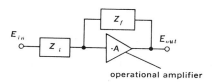

operational amplifier

If $|A| \gg 1$. $\dfrac{E_{out}}{E_{in}} \cong -\dfrac{Z_f}{Z_i}$

uration of the operational amplifier is illustrated. It can be shown that

$$E_o(s)/E_{in}(s) = -Z_f(s)/Z_i(s),$$

where $E_{in}(s), E_o(s)$ are respectively the input and output voltages and $Z_i(s)$, $Z_f(s)$ are the input and feedback impedances, all of these being functions of the complex variable s. See ANALOG COMPUTER.

operation code A sequence of characters that indicates some machine operation, generally included as part of an instruction.

operation decoder A device that on the basis of the operation code contained in a machine instruction chooses one or more control channels as necessary.

operation part Loosely, the part of an instruction that specifies the operation to be performed.

operation register In general, a register, not accessible to the programmer except for readout, in which the operation code for the next instruction to be executed is stored and decoded.

operations analysis OPERATIONS RESEARCH.

operations research The systematic study and analysis of the activities of systems composed of human beings, machines, and other resources, generally for the purpose of providing criteria for decisions intended to optimize system activity.

operator *n.* **1** A symbol that represents an operation to be performed on one or more operands. **2** One who operates a machine or mechanism.

operator command Any of various statements issued to the control program via a console device that causes requested information to be provided, new operations to be initiated, normal operations to be altered, or existing operations to be terminated.

OPM *abbr.* Operations per minute (equivalent to characters per minute when control functions are included).

optical character recognition Machine sensing and identification of printed characters by means of photoelectric devices.

optical reader A device that performs OPTICAL CHARACTER RECOGNITION.

optical scanner **1** A device that scans a pattern of incident light and generates an analog digital signal that is a function of the incident light and synchronized with the scan. **2** A device of this kind designated especially to generate digital representations of printed or written data.

optical type font A type font specially designed so that its characters are readily recognized both by human beings and machines.

optimize *v.* To cause (a system, process, or the like) to take on its most desirable configuration or operate in the best or most efficient way, in particular, to arrange (instructions and/or data) in storage so that a minimum of machine time is expended in accessing them.

OR **1** *n.* A logic operator having the property that if X is a statement, $P_1, P_2, \ldots P_n$ are statements, and X is equivalent to the OR of $P_1, P_2, \ldots P_n$, then X is true whenever at least one of the individual statements P_i is true. Compare EXCLUSIVE OR. **2** *abbr.* OPERATIONS RESEARCH.

order **1** *n.* An arrangement of a set of objects such that each one except the first (if there is a first) has a particular predecessor and each

except the last (if there is a last) has a particular successor. In this sense the set of all integers, positive and negative, has an order and lacks both a first and a last element. **2** *n.* An arrangement of two or more objects such that each object can be shown to be either a predecessor or successor (but not both) of any of the other objects. In this sense the fractions $\frac{1}{3}$, $\frac{1}{2}$, and $\frac{15}{16}$ are ordered. **3** *v.* To arrange (a set of objects) in either of these ways. **4** *n.* The property of a set whose elements are ordered. **5** *n.* Formerly, an INSTRUCTION. **6** *n.* Any of various ways in which things are ranked.

Truth table for
OR operator

A	B	A + B*
0	0	0
0	1	1
1	0	1
1	1	1

✻ A + B is symbolic notation for A **OR** B

organizing *adj.* SELF-ORGANIZING.

OR gate A hardware module that implements the operator OR.

orientation *n.* Of a teletypewriter, an adjustment of the time at which the receiving apparatus starts selection or of the time at which the start transition is made.

origin *n.* **1** The absolute storage address at which a program or block begins. **2** In relative coding, the absolute storage address to which addresses in a region are referenced. **3** On a system of rectangular coordinates, the point at which all the variables that can be represented have the value 0.

OS *abbr.* OPERATING SYSTEM.

oscilloscope *n.* An instrument in which the horizontal and vertical deflection of the electron beam of a cathode-ray tube are, respectively, proportional to a pair of applied voltages. In the most usual application of the instrument the vertical deflection is a signal voltage and the horizontal deflection is a linear time base.

outconnector *n.* On a flowchart, a connector indicating a point at which a flowline breaks for continuation elsewhere.

outline *n.* A CHARACTER OUTLINE.

output *n.* **1** That which is produced as the result of some process or operation, in particular, the results generated from the processing of a mass of data. **2** The transferral of data from internal to external storage.

output area A section of storage that has been set aside for output data.

output block An OUTPUT AREA.

output work queue A queue of control information that describes system output data sets, specifying to an OUTPUT WRITER their location and disposition.

output writer A job scheduler function that transcribes specified output data sets onto a system output unit independently of the program that generates the data.

overflow *n.* **1** The production of a result that exceeds the capacity of the register or storage area intended or reserved for it. **2** That part of a result which is lost when such a condition occurs.

overflow indicator A bistable device that changes state on the occurrence of an overflow in the register with which it is associated, designed so that its condition can be detected and so that it can be restored to its original condition.

overflow position In a storage register, a normally unused position capable of holding a digit produced by an overflow.

overlap *v.* To execute or perform (two or more operations) during the same time period, as, for example, to perform (input/output operations) while processing (computations).

overlay *n.* A technique in which the same area of main storage is used to hold different data and/or routines during the execution of the same program, each routine or data element being replaced when no longer needed.

overlay load module A load module that has been divided into overlay segments and which the linkage editor has provided with information that allows the overlay to cause each segment to be loaded at the proper time.

overlay supervisor A routine that controls the loading sequence and position of each segment of a program when overlay is being used.

overpunch *n.* See also MULTIPLE PUNCHING; ZONE PUNCH.

owned *adj.* In communications usage, unless otherwise modified, supplied by and belonging to a customer.

P

PABX *abbr.* PRIVATE AUTOMATIC BRANCH EX-CHANGE.

pack *v.* To transform (one or several associated items of data) into a representation that occupies less space in a storage medium than the original would have, but in such a way that the original representation can be completely reconstructed.

packing density The number of BITS stored per unit dimension of the storage medium, the demension used depending on the nature of the storage medium.

pad *n.* An ATTENUATOR.

pad character A character used to occupy time while some relatively slow function, generally mechanical in nature, is being performed.

padding *n.* **1** The filling of a block of storage with dummy data. **2** Any technique by means of which this is accomplished. **3** The dummy data so generated.

page *n.* Any of a number of blocks of arbitrary but uniform size into which core storage may be divided in order to facilitate the dynamic allocation of storage space.

page printer An output printing device that produces an entire page at one time.

panel *n.* A CONTROL PANEL.

paper tape reader A device that translates the perforations in a tape into a set of electrical impulses.

parallel *adj.* **1** Of or indicating two or more related processes or activities that occur simul-taneously. **2** Of or relating to simultaneity of processes. Compare SERIAL.

parallel addition A technique in which all the corresponding pairs of digits of two numbers being added are processed simultaneously during one cycle of execution, one or more subsequent cycles being used to propagate and adjust for any carries that may have been generated. Compare SERIAL ADDITION.

parallel computer **1** A computer having the capability of carrying on parallel logic or arith-metic operations. **2** Formerly, a computer that carried on some specified operation in parallel, as, for instance, a computer that handled all bits of a stored word at the same time.

parallel operation The simultaneous or con-current execution of two or more similar or re-lated operations, often by the use of multiple arithmetic or logic units.

parallel processing The simultaneous or con-current execution of two or more similar proc-esses, often by the use of such devices as multiple channels or multiple processing units.

parallel search storage A storage device in which queries are directed to one or more parts of all storage locations simultaneously.

parallel storage A storage device in which si-multaneous or concurrent access to words, digits, characters, bytes, or the like is possible.

parallel transmission In telecommunications, the simultaneous transmission of a number of elements all of which are parts of the same signal.

parameter *n.* **1** Any of the arbitrary constants used in writing an analytic expression. For instance in the expression

$$L\,di/dt + Ri = 0,$$

i is the independent variable while *L* and *R* are parameters. **2** A variable *t* such that given a function

$$y = f(x_1, x_2, \ldots x_n),$$

the function can be represented by the set of equations

$$y = g_0(t),\ x_1 = g_1(t),\ x_2 = g_2(t),\ \ldots x_n = g_n(t).$$

See FAMILY.

parametric *adj.* Of, using, or containing parameters.

parentheses-free notation PREFIX NOTATION.

parity *n.* The oddness or evenness of a number.

parity bit An extra bit appended to an array of bits in such a way that the sum of all the bits is either always odd or always even, used for purposes of error detection.

parity check An error-detection technique that tests whether the sum of an array of bits is of the correct parity.

part *n.* An ADDRESS PART or OPERATION PART.

partial carry In parallel addition, an arrangement in which the propagation of some or all of the carries is temporarily inhibited, the carries being stored for a time instead.

partial derivative Of a FUNCTION of a set of independent variables $x_1, x_2, \ldots x_n$, the DERIVATIVE

$$fx_i(x_1, x_2, \ldots x_n) = Dx_i(x_1, x_2, \ldots x_n) = f_i(x_1, x_2, \ldots x_n)$$
$$= \partial f(x_1, x_2, \ldots x_n)/\partial x$$

taken with respect to one of these variables x_i, with all of the others held constant.

partial differential equation A differential equation that contains more than one independent variable and/or derivatives or differentials of more than one independent variable.

partition *v.* To subdivide (a large block) into subunits for more convenient handling.

pass *n.* A single processing of a body of data, as in assembly where some operations are performed on the source program in a first processing and other operations are performed in a second processing.

patch **1** *v.* To make some change or correction in (a routine), often in a way that is temporary, rough, or expeditious. **2** *n.* A change or correction made in this way. **3** *n.* An electrical connection made by some temporary means.

patch panel A CONTROL PANEL.

path *n.* The course of logic of sequence of instructions used by a computer in a particular execution of a routine.

pattern recognition The automatic sensing and identification of forms, shapes, arrangements, and the like.

pattern-sensitive fault A fault whose occurrence is associated with some particular data pattern.

PAX *abbr.* PRIVATE AUTOMATIC EXCHANGE.

PBX *abbr.* PRIVATE BRANCH EXCHANGE.

PCM *abbr.* **1** Punched card machine. **2** PULSE CODE MODULATION.

peek-a-boo A method in which two cards are compared by superimposing them to determine if they are punched in any corresponding positions.

perforator *n.* A device that produces holes, as in cards or paper tape, for the purpose of representing data.

peripheral equipment In a data processing system, any of the various items of hardware that are distinct from the central processing unit and which may provide the system with increased storage capacity or with input/output capability.

peripheral transfer The transmission of data between peripheral units.

permanent dynamic storage A form of dynamic storage, as a magnetic disc or drum storage, in which the maintenance of the stored data does not depend on a flow of energy.

permanent storage FIXED STORAGE.

permutation *n.* Any ordered arrangement of all or some of the members of a set.

PH *abbr.* PHASE.

phantom channel A communications channel for which no independent conductive path exists. The signal information for such a channel is added to that of other channels in such a way that no additional paths are required but all signals are recoverable with negligible interaction. (See illustration on following page.)

phase *n.* Of a simple harmonic motion of the form

$$u = \cos(\omega t + k\phi)$$

the angle $\omega t + k\phi$. The phase of a sinusoidal function of time relates the function to a fixed instant of time or to another sinusoid of the same frequency. It is usual to express phase as an angle θ such that $0 < \theta < 2\pi$. Thus $\theta = \omega t + k\phi - n2\pi$ where n is such an integer as is needed to place θ in the desired interval.

phase distortion In a transmission system, a form of distortion that results when different frequency components of a signal propagate through the system at different speeds, thus changing their phases relative to one another.

phase modulation A form of MODULATION in which the phase of the carrier is varied according to the information to be transmitted. Analytically, if a modulation function $m(t)$ is defined, a phase-modulated carrier $P(t)$ is given by

$$P(t) = A_0 \cos [\omega_0 t + \Delta \theta\, m(t)],$$

where $\Delta \theta$ defines the amount of phase shift per unit change in the modulation function. As frequency is the derivative with respect to time of phase, phase modulation and frequency modulation are closely related.

physical record A record defined in terms of physical parameters and variations of physical parameters rather than in terms of its logical content.

pinboard *n.* A perforated board into which pins can be manually inserted in such a way as to control the operation of equipment.

pinfeed platen A platen that drives paper by engaging rows of holes punched in it on rings of pins rather than by friction.

pitch *n.* ROW PITCH.

PL/I *abbr.* PROGRAMMING LANGUAGE I.

plant *n.* In common carrier usage, the physical equipment and personnel which together comprise a communication system.

platen *n.* A backing, generally cylindrical in form, that serves to support the paper stock upon which a printing mechanism strikes in order to produce an impression.

plot **1** *v.* To produce a map, graph, or diagram of, as of a function on rectangular coordinates.

PHANTOM CHANNEL

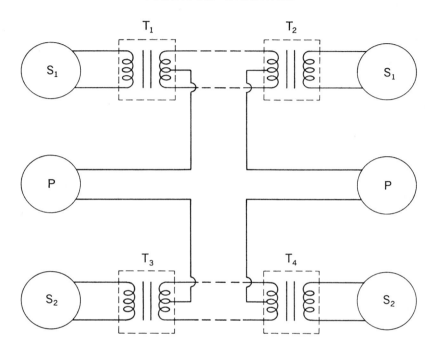

one method of obtaining a phantom channel
S_1 terminals of side circuit 1, S_2 terminals of side circuit 2,
P terminals of phantom channel, $T_{1,2,3,4}$ repeating coils.
Since the current associated with the phantom channel appears
in equal strength and opposite phases on both sides of the
center-tapped windings of the repeating coils, it cancels
itself in the other windings and has a negligible effect on
the side circuits.

2 *n.* The map, diagram, or graph so produced.

plugboard *n.* A board having an array of jacks into which plugs can be manually inserted in order to control equipment.

plug-in A PLUG-IN UNIT.

plug-in unit A self-contained circuit module, so designed that it can be readily connected with other equipment, often literally plugging into place.

plus *adj.* A word placed before a number to indicate that it is positive. In practice *plus* is often not stated but is understood by implication.

plus sign The character + used to indicate PLUS.

PMS *abbr.* PUBLIC MESSAGE SERVICE.

point *n.* **1** An explicitly defined location, as on a coordinate system, in a routine, in space, etc. **2** In positional notation the character . , either explicitly stated or implied, used to separate the integral and fractional parts of a numerical expression.

point-to-point transmission The direct transmission of data between two points without the use of intervening terminals or computers.

polar *adj.* Of or possessing the quality of being positive or negative, as an electric charge or flow of current.

polar relay A relay whose armature is biased into a center position by means of a permanent magnet and moves in one of two directions depending on the polarity of the applied current.

polar transmission **1** In teletypewriter transmission a method of signalling in which a MARK is represented by a direct current of one polarity and a SPACE by a direct current of the opposite polarity, the absence of current flow indicating a no-signal condition. **2** By extension, any signalling system that uses three distinct conditions, one representing a MARK, another a SPACE, and a third a no-signal condition.

Polish notation PREFIX NOTATION.

polling *n.* A technique in which each of the terminals that share a common line is periodically interrogated in order to determine if it requires any service.

portable data medium A data medium designed to be readily separable from the device that performs read and write operations on it, and to be easily transportable as well.

position *n.* Any location in a string that is identifiable, generally by means of an assigned serial number, and can be occupied by a character or bit.

positional notation A method in which a number is represented by an ordered set of digits in such a way that the value contributed by each digit is a function of its position as well as its identity.

positional representation POSITIONAL NOTATION.

positive feedback See FEEDBACK.

post *v.* To enter (a unit of information) into a record.

postmortem *adj.* Of, indicating, or having to do with the analysis of an operation subsequent to its completion.

postmortem dump A static dump executed at the end of a machine run for debugging purposes.

power **1** *n.* The number of times some quantity is taken as a factor in forming the expression for another quantity, generally indicated by an exponent. If *p, q* are understood to be any integers and *a, b* are any positive numbers, then the following statements are true:

$$a^0 = 1; \quad a^p a^q = a^{p+q}; \quad a^p/a^q = a^{p-q}; \quad (a^p)^q = a^{pq};$$
$$(ab)^p = a^p b^p; \quad (a/b)^p = a^p/b^p.$$

It can be shown that the above statements also hold if a^{-p} is defined as $1/a^p$ and $a^{1/p}$ is defined as $\sqrt[p]{a}$. Similarly we can define $a^{p/q}$ as $(\sqrt[q]{a})^p$. It is also possible to extend the above definitions in such a way that numbers can have powers that are IRRATIONAL NUMBERS and COMPLEX NUMBERS. **2** In physics, the rate at which work is done with respect to time.

power level At a point in a transmission system, the ratio of the signal power at that point to some level of power chosen as a reference. This reference level is generally chosen as one WATT or one milliwatt and the ratio expressed in decibels.

precedence prosign A group of characters attached to a message to indicate to communications personnel how it is to be handled.

precision *n.* The amount of information implicit in the statement of a numerical quantity, for example a three-digit binary numeral indicates one of eight possibilities, while a three-digit decimal numeral indicates one of 1,000 possibilities. In the determination of precision it is important to distinguish between significant and nonsignificant zeros. Strictly speaking there is a difference of precision between 1,000 and 1. $\times 10^3$; in the first case the low-order zeros are known to have that value while in the second case all that is known is the explicit digit and the multiplier. To express the first number in notation equivalent to that of the second it is necessary to write 1.000×10^3. See DOUBLE PRECISION.

predefined process A process whose identifi-

cation is but symbolic and whose definition is located elsewhere, for instance in the FORTRAN instruction Y. = SQRT X. (translated *Y*, a floating point number, is to be set equal to the square root of *X*, also a floating point number), SQRT serves to identify the process *square root* whose actual definition is contained in a subroutine supplied by the compiler.

prefix notation A method of forming mathematical expressions in which each operator precedes the operands with which it is associated.

preset *v.* To initialize (various conditions or values), as for instance the control values of a loop.

prestore *v.* INITIALIZE.

presumptive address A REFERENCE ADDRESS.

preventive maintenance Any maintenance performed on a system in order to prevent failures rather than to correct them after they occur.

preventive maintenance time Time, generally allotted by schedule, in which preventive maintenance is performed.

primary center A control center that connects toll centers, also sometimes serving as a toll center for its local end offices; a class 3 office.

primary storage The main internal storage.

prime number Any integer such that its only integral factors are itself and 1.

primitive *n.* A FUNCTION $F(x)$ of which the function $f(x)$ under consideration is the DERIVATIVE.

print contrast ratio In optical character recognition, the ratio of the difference between the maximum reflectance in a specified area and the reflectance at a specified point and the neighborhood surrounding that point to the maximum reflectance in that specified area.

print control character Any of the various control characters that affect printing operations.

printer *n.* Any of various devices that translate coded characters into HARD COPY.

print-out Printed hard copy produced as output by a data-processing machine or system.

priority indicator 1 A group of characters attached to a message to indicate its relative priority with respect to use of the transmission facilities. 2 An item of information used to establish the ordering of a QUEUE.

priority scheduling system A type of JOB SCHEDULER designed to improve system performance by means of input and output work queues.

private *adj.* Leased from a common carrier for the exclusive use of one customer.

private automatic branch exchange A private automatic telephone exchange that implements the transmission of calls to and from the public telephone system.

private automatic exchange A dial telephone exchange that provides private service but lacks the capability of transmitting calls to and from the public telephone system.

private branch exchange A manually operated telephone exchange connected to the public system on the customer's premises and operated by customer supplied personnel.

private line The communications channel and associated equipment furnished to a customer for his exclusive use, excluding interexchange switching arrangements.

private line service 1 Communications service supplied for the exclusive use of a particular customer. 2 The providing of circuits for such use.

privileged instruction Any of various instructions that are inaccessible to the problem program, their use being reserved to the supervisory routine.

probability theory The branch of mathematics concerned with the assignment of numbers that represent the relative probabilities of chance events, the laws governing such assignments being statistical in nature and thus inapplicable in an absolute way to individual events or items.

problem *n.* 1 A question or proposition to which a solution or answer is required, one or more operations being necessary to provide the solution or answer if such is at all available. 2 A BENCHMARK PROBLEM.

problem description A statement of a problem, often including such details as a description of the method of solution, the necessary procedures and algorithms, and the like.

problem-oriented language Any of various programming languages each of which is designed to be conveniently used in the expression and programming of problems of a given type.

problem program A program whose execution is expected to solve a problem, more specifically, any routine that is distinctly separate from the OPERATING SYSTEM.

procedure *n.* 1 A sequence of actions designed to solve a problem or some part thereof. 2 An INLINE PROCEDURE.

procedure-oriented language Any of various programming languages each of which is designed to be conveniently used in the expression and programming of procedures that are applicable to a broad class of problems.

process *n.* A sequence of operations designed

to occur systematically and produce a desired result.

process chart A FLOWCHART or BLOCK DIAGRAM.

process control The control of a continuous process by automatic means. See NUMERICAL CONTROL; FEEDBACK CONTROL SYSTEM.

processing program Any routine other than a control routine; a problem program.

process-limited Indicating a data-processing system whose overall speed is limited by the speed of the central processing unit rather than by the speed of the input/output devices.

processor *n.* 1 A DATA PROCESSOR. 2 A computer program that performs compilation, assembly, translation, and similar operations for some programming language such as FOR–TRAN or COBOL.

process time The time required for compilation or assembly of a source program.

product *n.* The result of multiplying a pair of quantities together.

product area In certain computers, an area of main storage in which the results of multiplication operations are automatically stored.

production time The part of OPERATING TIME that excludes DEVELOPMENT TIME and MAKEUP TIME.

program 1 *n.* An ordered set of actions or operations designed to yield a desired result. 2 *n.* A computer ROUTINE. 3 *v.* To design and verify the operation of a program or programs for the solution of (a problem or problems).

program address register A register in which the address of the machine instruction currently being executed is stored.

programatics *n.* The discipline that deals with the study of the techniques of programming and programming languages.

program generator A generalized program by means of which the computer itself can prepare other programs.

program library An organized collection of proven computer programs and routines.

programmed check A checking or debugging procedure designed by the programmer as a part of his program.

programmer *n.* 1 One who prepares a program. 2 A specialist whose main occupation is the design, writing, and testing of programs.

programming *n.* The design, writing, and verification of the effectiveness of programs.

programming language An artificial language designed to be conveniently used by human beings in programming some class of problems.

Programming Language/ I A high level programming language designed for application to a large class of problems.

program module A discrete, identifiable segment of a program, generally treated as a unit by the operating system or other software routines.

program-sensitive fault A fault whose occurrence is associated with the execution of some particular sequence of program steps.

propagation constant A characteristic γ of a transmission line or medium that indicates its effect on a wave that is propagating through it. For example the voltage (or current) x received a distance d from the sending end of a transmission line is given by

$$x = x_0 e^{-d\gamma},$$

where x_0 is the wave amplitude at the sending end and γ is a complex number given by

$$\gamma = \alpha + j\beta.$$

The attenuation in nepers per unit distance is

given by α; the phase shift per unit distance is given by β. In a transmission line it can be shown that

$$\gamma = \sqrt{ZY}$$

where Z is series impedance per unit distance and Y shunt admittance per unit distance. Similarly in a vacuum

$$\gamma = \sqrt{\mu_0/\epsilon_0},$$

where μ_0, ϵ_0 are respectively the permeability and permittivity of a vacuum. The term propagation *constant* is somewhat of a misnomer, as γ, in general, can vary with position, direction, and frequency.

propagation delay The T time required for a signal to propagate between two points, given in general by $T = d\beta/\omega$, where d is the distance between the points, ω equals 2π times the frequency in hertz, and β is the imaginary part of the PROPAGATION CONSTANT.

proper fraction A fraction indicated as the ratio of two integers where the numerator is smaller than the denominator.

proper subset Of a set A, any subset A_1 such that A intersection A_1 is not identical with A.

proportional band In a feedback control system, the range of values of the controlled variable through which the output controller will operate without saturation.

proportional control system A type of feedback control system in which the correction generated is a linear function of the original error.

protected location A storage location in which all write operations are inhibited automatically unless a special code or control word has been supplied in advance to the supervisory software.

pseudo code A code that is unacceptable

for execution unless translation is performed.

pseudo-random number sequence A sequence of numbers generated by some defined arithmetic process and which is sufficiently random to be considered as such for some particular purpose, the characteristic of "sufficient randomness" often being determined on the basis of how closely the sequence satisfies some one of the statistical distributions defined as random distribution.

Public Message Service The public telegraph system operated by Western Union.

public switched network A switched message network that provides service to a large number of customers.

pulse *n.* A waveform consisting of the sum of a positive step function and a negative step function separated in time.

pulse code modulation A form of pulse modulation in which the information to be transmitted is represented by characters, each character being represented in turn by some combination of pulses.

pulse modulation A form of modulation in which a carrier is permitted to vary between two or more discrete states. The information-bearing characteristic of the pulses thus generated may be amplitude, frequency, phase, width, count, or some combination of these. See PULSE CODE MODULATION.

pulse repetition rate The rate with respect to time at which some source generates pulses.

punch **1** *n.* A small hole, as in a card or paper tape. See DIGIT PUNCH; KEYPUNCH; X-PUNCH; Y-PUNCH; ZONE PUNCH. **2** *v.* To make such a hole in (a card or tape).

punched card **1** A card on which data is represented as a pattern of holes. **2** Such a card even before the actual punching process has been carried out.

punched tape Tape on which data is represented by a pattern of holes or cuts. Also called perforated tape.

punching position A PUNCH POSITION.

punch position On a card or tape, a point at which or an area within which, a punch can represent data.

pushbutton dialing The use of an array of keys or buttons rather than a rotary dial to generate the digit sequence that establishes a circuit connection, the digits themselves usually being coded as tone sequences.

pushbutton dialing pad The array of twelve keys used in PUSHBUTTON DIALING.

pushdown dialing PUSHBUTTON DIALING.

pushdown list A list constructed and maintained on a "last in, first out" basis, that is, in such a way that the item next to be retrieved is the most recently stored.

pushdown store A storage device that acts in the manner of a PUSHDOWN LIST.

pushup list A list constructed and maintained on a "first in, first out" basis, that is, in such a way that the item next to be retrieved and removed is the oldest still contained in the list.

put *v.* To place (a single data record) into an output file.

Q

QCB *abbr.* QUEUE CONTROL BLOCK.

QTAM *abbr.* Queued Telecommunications Access Method.

quad *n.* A set of four separately insulated conductors twisted together, used as a structural element in forming cables.

quadratic *adj.* Indicating or relating to a function of the form $f(x) = ax^2 + bx + c$, where $a \neq 0$.

quadratic programming In operations research, a special case of NONLINEAR PROGRAMMING in which either the object function or one or more of its constraints is quadratic, none of them being of any higher degree.

qualified name A data name that carries an explicit restriction to the class of data to which it is applied in a given classification system.

qualifier *n.* In a QUALIFIED NAME, any of the component names other than the last (the rightmost). See SIMPLE NAME.

quantity *n.* A symbol or expression that is concerned with value rather than with the relations between such symbols or expressions.

quantization *n.* The process or result of quantizing.

quantization error QUANTIZATION UNCERTAINTY.

quantization uncertainty A measure of the uncertainty, that is, of the irretrievable information loss, that occurs as a result of the quantization of a function in an interval where it is continuous.

quantize *v.* To operate on a (function) in such a way as to convert it into a discrete set of values connected by step functions, that is, for example, given a function $f(x)$, which may or may not be continuous and differentiable, and a second function $g(x)$ such that if

$$a_i \leq f(x) < a_{i+1}, g(x) = a_i,$$

where a_i is one of a set of n nonoverlapping intervals in a, and it is understood that $f(x)$ is successively evaluated at $x_0, x_0 + \Delta x, \ldots x_0 + n\Delta x, g(x)$ is a quantized version of $f(x)$. Clearly $g(x)$ is an approximation of $f(x)$, the closeness of the approximation depending on the magnitudes of the intervals in a and x. Thus the transformation of $f(x)$ into $g(x)$ may irreversibly destroy some of the information in $f(x)$. See SAMPLING THEOREM.

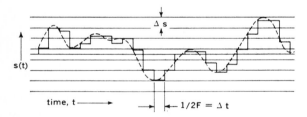

A quantized waveform

quantized *adj.* Restricted to a discrete set of values.

quantizer *n.* One who or that which quantizes, in particular, an analog-to-digital CONVERTER.

quantum *n.* One of the intervals a_i used to QUANTIZE a function.

quantum clock In a data-processing system that uses time sharing, a device that allocates an interval of processing time to each program.

quarter speed A speed equal to 25% of the rated speed of the associated equipment, in particular, in transoceanic telegraph, 12.5 bauds, 25% of full speed.

quarter-squares multiplier In analog computers, a multiplication unit that operates by means of the identity

$$x y \equiv \tfrac{1}{4}((x + y)^2 - (x - y)^2).$$

quasi instruction In a source program, an expression which is similar or identical in form to an instruction but for which there will be no corresponding machine instruction in the object program, in effect, an instruction directed to the assembler or compiler.

queue 1 *n.* An ordered sequence of items waiting to be serviced according to their order. **2** *v.* To form or arrange in a queue.

queue control block A control block used in the regulation of the sequential use of some programmer-defined facility by a set of competing tasks.

queued access method An access method that automatically synchronizes the transfer of data between a program and input/output facilities, thus eliminating processing delays caused by input/output operations.

queueing theory The mathematical theory dealing with the study of the formation and behavior of queues or waiting lines; also, loosely, CONGESTION THEORY.

quiescing *n.* The halting of a multiprogrammed system by means of the rejection of new jobs.

QUIKTRAN A programming language that is essentially a subset of FORTRAN, used principally when a number of terminals use a single central processor on a time-sharing basis, the response time at any one terminal being sufficiently short that each user is unaware of the others. This language is especially suitable for use in CONVERSATIONAL MODE.

quinary *adj.* Biquinary. See BIQUINARY CODE.

quotient *n.* The quantity that appears as a result of a division operation.

R

radical *n.* A quantity that is equal to a root of another quantity, as indicated by a radical sign.

radical sign The sign $\sqrt[n]{\ }$ used to indicate the *n*th root of a quantity, the value of *n* being understood by implication when $n = 2$.

radicand *n.* The quantity whose ROOT is indicated by a radical sign.

radix *n.* A number on which a system of numerations is founded, that is, a number *b* such that any integer is of the form $d_0 + d_1b + d_2b^2 \ldots + d_nb^n$, where $d_1, d_2, \ldots d_n$ are non-negative integers smaller than *b*.

radix complement See COMPLEMENT.

radix-minus-one complement See COMPLEMENT.

radix notation A form of positional representation in which the ratio of the significances of any pair of adjacent digit positions is equal to the RADIX of the system of numeration.

radix point In radix notation, a character (.), explicit or implied, that separates the digits representing the integral part of a number from those representing the fractional part.

rain barrel effect An echo-like effect imparted to an audio signal that passes over an im-

properly compensated or terminated transmission line as a result of repeated signal reflections.

random access Indicating a storage medium or device in which the time necessary to store or gain access to any particular item of data is, in effect, independent of the storage location and the history of the system.

random access device A device in which access time is, in effect, independent of data location and system history.

random number generator In general, an analog device whose output is a randomly changing variable, operating, usually, from an electrical noise source whose output is band-limited or demodulated in some manner.

random numbers A succession of digits or numbers obtained entirely as a result of a chance process. While there is no known rigorous and absolute definition of what constitutes a sequence of random numbers, the satisfaction of various statistical criteria is considered an adequate test of randomness.

random processing The treatment of data independently of its location in external storage, the order of processing being determined by an arbitrary sequence of input data in conjunction with which the stored data is to be processed.

random-walk method A special case of the Monte Carlo method in which a problem is given a probabilistic solution. The "walk" consists of a series of traverses along line segments whose directions (and possibly also lengths) vary at random. It can be shown that the probability of reaching a defined point by such a walk at a given time is often given by a function that is for other reasons of interest.

range *n.* **1** In mathematics, the set of all values that the DEPENDENT VARIABLE of a FUNCTION can assume. **2** The absolute value of the difference between the extreme values included in such a set. **3** Loosely, the set of all values that a variable can take. Compare DOMAIN.

range finder On a teletypewriter receiver, a mechanism that permits the receiver-distributor face to be moved through an arc equal to the length of a unit segment. Its normal adjustment is that which will produce optimum results under a given set of operating line conditions.

rank **1** *v.* To arrange (a set of items) in order according to some criterion such as importance, complexity, or the like. **2** *n.* Any of the positions in an ordered set whose order depends on importance, complexity, or the like. **3** *v.* To assign (an item) a position in such an ordered set.

rate action In a control system, corrective action that is proportional to the DERIVATIVE with respect to time of the ERROR SIGNAL.

rate center In a telephone system, any of the various specified geographic locations used in the measurement of mileage for the application of interexchange mileage rates.

rated speed NOMINAL SPEED.

ratio *n.* The quotient of a pair of numbers or quantities.

rational number Any number that can be expressed as an indicated quotient of p and q, where p and q are both integers.

raw data Data which has been subjected to neither processing nor reduction.

read **1** *v.* To obtain (data) from some source, as, for instance, a data medium or storage device. **2** *n.* The operation of reading.

read-around ratio In an electrostatic storage, each time a particular location is interrogated the spillover of electrons tends to degrade the data in surrounding locations, making its periodic restoration necessary. The read-around ratio is the number of times a location can be interrogated for each such restoration.

reader *n.* A device that accepts information stored in one form and converts it to another form.

reader/interpreter The part of the control program that handles the reading, transcription, and interpretation of an input job stream and the associated job control statements.

read-only storage FIXED STORAGE.

ready condition The condition of a task when all of its requirements for execution other than control of the central processor have been satisfied.

real number Any member of the set that contains all the RATIONAL NUMBERS and irrational numbers.

real time **1** Time as it relates to actual physical processes. **2** Of, indicating, or related to data-processing systems that are able to perform computations rapidly enough to allow the results to be useful in the control of physical processes.

real-time input Data generated as a result of a physical process occurring in real time and inserted into a data-processing system at the time of its generation.

real-time output Output data computed from real-time input and delivered to another system as necessary. In general, the time lag between the generation of real-time input and the delivery of real-time output is negligible from the point of view of the system that generates the input and receives the output.

received data lead One of the basic data set interchange leads defined in EIA Standard RS–232–B.

receive-only Indicating or relating to a device that can receive signals but lacks transmission capability.

receive-only typing reperforator A teletypewriter receiver whose output consists of perforated tape with characters printed along its edge.

receiving-end crossfire In a telegraph channel, CROSSFIRE introduced at a terminal remote from the transmitter.

receiving margin In telegraph applications, the practical range of adjustment of the RANGE FINDER, generally about 75 points on a 120-point scale for a machine in correct adjustment.

receiving perforator A REPERFORATOR.

record *n.* A data unit composed of a set of related items.

record gap On a data medium, an area used to separate adjacent blocks or records, or to indicate the end of a block or record. Generally such an area is left blank or otherwise distinctly identified.

recording density In a data medium that is divided into linear tracks, the number of bits per unit length of a linear track.

recording trunk A trunk connecting a local telephone central office or private branch exchange to a long distance office, reserved for communication between operators.

record layout **1** The manner in which the data composing a RECORD is arranged and structured. **2** By extension, the description of a RECORD.

record length The size of a RECORD, generally given in units such as WORDS or characters.

record separator A character intended for the demarcation of the logical boundary between RECORDS.

rectangular coordinates A set of three lines (axes) that intersect at a common point in space in such a way that each line (axis), is perpendicular to the plane containing the other two. The position of any point in the space occupied by the axes can be defined with respect to the point of mutual intersection (the origin) by drawing the line segment connecting the point to the origin and noting the length of its projection on each of the axes. In a very common special case, the length of the projection on one axis is zero for all points and the system then refers to a set of points in a plane. Conceptually, if not in physical representation, the system can be extended to a space of more than three dimensions.

red-tape operations HOUSEKEEPING.

reduction *n.* DATA REDUCTION.

redundancy *n.* In information theory, the extent to which a communications or message source overspecifies information. More precisely, redundancy *r* is given by

$$r = 1 - H/H^{max},$$

where *H* is the information rate of the channel and H^{max} is the theoretical maximum information rate of the channel when coded in the same way. Broadly speaking, redundancy makes it increasingly likely that errors will be detected.

redundancy check An automatic or programmed check based on the systematic insertion of redundant characters in a way designed for checking purposes.

redundant *adj.* Of, indicating, or related to those elements contained in a message or transmitted by a communications source which contributes to redundancy.

reed relay A switching device consisting of magnetic contactors sealed into a glass tube, the contactors being actuated by the magnetic field of an external solenoid, electromagnet, or permanent magnet.

contacts

reed switch A REED RELAY.

reel *n.* A cylindrical mounting with flanges at each end, designed to hold a roll of tape.

reenterable load module A LOAD MODULE that can be used concurrently by two or more tasks.

reference level RELATIVE TRANSMISSION LEVEL.

reference noise In an electric circuit, that level of noise power that produces on a noise meter (a meter having specifically defined characteristics, such as transient response, frequency response, etc.), a reading equivalent to that produced by 10 picowatts of electric power at 1000 hz.

reference volume For a complex electric waveform, such as that corresponding to speech or music, the amount of power that gives a reading of 0 VU on a standard VOLUME INDICATOR.

refile *n.* The transmission of a message from a station on a leased line network to a station not on that network, usually accomplished by retransmission as a telegram through a preselected Western Union office.

reflected binary code GRAY CODE.

regen *n.* A REGENERATIVE REPEATER.

regeneration *n.* **1** The restoration of data that has been somehow degraded while in storage. **2** The restoration of a pulse waveform that has become degraded due to parasitic effects on a transmission line.

regenerative repeater A telegraph REPEATER that subjects signals to REGENERATION as well as amplification.

region *n.* In relative coding, a group of addresses which are all referred to the same BASE ADDRESS.

regional center In the telephone network, a control center (class 1 office) that connects sectional centers.

register **1** *n.* A storage device designed for some specified amount of data, as, for example, one word. **2** *v.* To place in a position that is accurate and correct with respect to some reference.

registration *n.* **1** The process of registering. **2** The accuracy or precision with which this has been accomplished: poor *registration*.

regulation *n.* **1** Automatic compensation for changes in a dynamic variable, as for example, variation in the equalization applied to a cable in order to compensate for the changes in loss as the cable temperature varies. **2** The stability of some parameter whether or not automatically controlled: the voltage *regulation* of a power source.

relative address The numerical difference between an ABSOLUTE ADDRESS and a BASE ADDRESS.

relative coding CODING in which MACHINE INSTRUCTIONS with RELATIVE ADDRESSES are used.

relative transmission level The ratio, in decibels, between the levels of test-tone power measured at two different points in a transmission system, the power level at the transmitting switchboard frequently being taken as the reference point for 0 db.

relay *n.* An electrically operated mechanical switch.

relay center A central point at which messages are switched; a message-switching center.

reliability *n.* The probability that a device or system will operate over a specified time or period of duty without failure. See MEAN TIME BETWEEN FAILURES.

relocate *v.* In programming, to transfer a routine from one area of storage to another, adjusting address references so that the routine is executable in its new location.

relocation dictionary The data (actually part of the module itself) that identifies all the address constants in an object module or load module that are subject to relocation.

remote access Indicating terminals from which communication with a data-processing facility located at some distance is possible.

remote station The data terminal equipment necessary for communication with a data-processing facility that is located at some distance.

repeater *n.* A device that automatically receives and retransmits electrical or electromagnetic signals, generally with amplification and often with REGENERATION as well.

repeating coil In telecommunications, an audio-frequency transformer having a ratio of 1:1 between its primary and secondary windings, used in the implementation of simplex and phantom circuits.

reperforator *n.* An automatic device that translates coded electrical signals into a series of perforations in a tape.

reperforator/transmitter An item of teletypewriter equipment consisting of a reperforator and a tape transmitter, each operating independently of the other, used as a relaying device, for establishing compatibility between differing rates of transmission and reception, and in temporary queueing.

repertory *n.* INSTRUCTION REPERTORY.

repetition instruction An instruction that causes some set of instructions to be executed an indicated number of times.

report generation A technique by means of which a complete machine report is produced using a description of the input file and of the content and format of the output report.

report generator A routine that implements REPORT GENERATION.

report program generator A software routine designed to handle the production of output reports, but having great generality as to the types and numbers of input/output units it can accommodate.

reproduce *v.* To duplicate (stored information), especially information stored on punched cards, punched paper tape, or magnetic tape.

reproducer *n.* A device that is capable of duplicating the information contained on a punched card on another card, entirely or in part.

request to send One of the basic data set leads defined in EIA Standard RS–232–B.

rerun *n.* A repetition of a machine run, often because of a correction, an error, or the like. Also called ROLLBACK.

rerun point In a computer program, that location in the instruction sequence at which either the program itself or a restart routine has access to all the information pertinent to the rerunning of the program.

reset *v.* 1 To put (a storage device) back into some prescribed initial condition, not necessarily the condition that represents zero. 2 To put (a binary storage location) into the condition that represents zero.

reset rate In a control system, the number of corrective actions per unit time.

residual error ratio The ERROR RATIO that results after attempts at correction have been made.

residue check A check in which the remainder obtained by dividing each operand by n (an arbitrary integer) is used for checking purposes.

resolution *n.* A figure of merit for a system indicating the smallest input change that is detectable, while not necessarily measurable, at the output. It can be shown that this figure is essentially a function of the gain and noise figure of the system.

resolver *n.* A device that can be arranged in such a way that if its input is a VECTOR, it delivers two outputs, each proportional to a component of the vector.

resource *n.* In a computing system or operating system, any facility required by a job or task.

resource manager In a control routine, any function responsible for the allocation of a system resource.

response *n.* SPECTRAL RESPONSE.

response time 1 The time that elapses between the generation of an inquiry at some terminal and the receipt of a reply at that terminal. 2 The time that elapses between the generation of a message at some terminal and its reception at the point to which it is addressed.

restart *v.* To restore (a routine) to the condition of being executed, the data used being that recorded at a CHECKPOINT.

restore *v.* RESET.

retrieval *n.* INFORMATION RETRIEVAL.

return *n.* CARRIAGE RETURN.

return code A code designed to affect the execution of subsequently run routines.

return code resister A register designed or used for the storage of a RETURN CODE.

return-to-reference recording A method of magnetic recording in which any adjacent pair of binary digits is separated by a brief return to a reference condition of magnetization.

return-to-zero recording A special case of

RETURN-TO-REFERENCE recording in which the reference condition is zero magnetization.

reusable routine A routine that can be used by two or more tasks.

reverse channel In a HALF-DUPLEX data-transmission system, a channel by means of which the receiver can communicate with the transmitter, used in conjunction with Bell System data sets and, generally, only for the transmission of control information.

reverse direction flow On a flowchart, any flow that proceeds other than from left to right or top to bottom.

rewind *v.* To return (a magnetic or paper tape) to its beginning.

ring counter A counting circuit consisting of N bistable outputs arranged so that one and only one output is "on" at a particular time. In response to an input pulse the "on" condition is shifted to the next stage in the sequence, the first stage being the successor of the last.

ringdown *n.* In a telephone network, a method of selectively signalling subscribers connected to the same line by making their equipment sensitive to ringing currents of different frequencies (generally submultiples of one frequency) or of differently modulated forms of the same frequency.

ring of integers A set of integers on which there are defined two operations, "$\times$" (equivalent to multiplication), and "$+$" (equivalent to addition) where the following requirements are satisfied:
1) If a and b are members of the set, then $a + b$ and $a \times b$ are also members of the set.
2) $a + b = b + a$.
3) If c is also a member of the set, then $(a + b) + c = a + (b + c)$.

4) There exists in the set an element 0 such that $a + 0 = a$, where a is an arbitrarily chosen member of the set.
5) For any a in the set there exists an element x such that $a + x = 0$.
6) $(a \times b) \times c = a(b \times c)$.
7) $a \times (b + c) = a \times b + a \times c$; $(b + c) \times a = b \times a + c \times a$.
In addition a ring may also have the properties:
8) $a \times b = b \times a$
9) For any a in the set there exists an element e such that $a \times e = e \times a = a$.
It can be shown that if properties 8 and 9 are included, the set of all integers is a ring with respect to this definition.

ring of integers modulo *n.* A ring of integers derived from the set of all integers according to the following rule: Let n be an integer greater than 1 and a and b be two other integers; if n is a factor of $a - b$, then a is said to be congruent to b modulo n. For example, $18 = 3 \pmod 5$, $1342 = 2 \pmod 5$, etc. It can be verified that the set derived in this way is a ring of integers and that the largest integer it contains is $n - 1$. See RESIDUE CHECK.

ring shift An END-AROUND SHIFT.

RO *abbr.* RECEIVE-ONLY.

rollback *n.* A programmed return to a checkpoint located earlier in a routine.

roll in To replace in main storage (data) which had been transferred to auxiliary storage.

roll out To transfer into an auxiliary storage (data) contained in main storage.

root *n.* **1** A number that produces a given number when taken as a factor an indicated number of times; as an example 2 is a 4th root of 16. It is a general truth that a given number has as many roots as the order of the root that is extracted, although some of these roots are complex numbers that occur in pairs such that each is the CONJUGATE of the other. **2** Of an algebraic equation, any number which when substituted for the unknown variable transforms the equation into an identity.

root segment **1** The part of an overlay program that remains in main throughout execution of the entire program. **2** The first segment of an overlay program.

rotary dial In a switched communication system, the spring-loaded rotary mechanism that can be hand-operated to produce groups of pulses that identify the called station as in a conventional telephone system.

ROTR *abbr.* RECEIVE-ONLY TYPING REPERFORATOR.

round *v.* To adjust (a number) to a lower order of precision by dropping one or more of the least significant digits and compensating for their absence in some way. In one method 5 is added to the digit following the last digit to be retained and a 1 is carried if it occurs. Thus 2.7345 would become 2.735, while 2.7344 would become 2.734.

rounding error An error that results from the rounding of one or more numbers.

round off To ROUND.

routine *n.* A sequence of instructions designed to accomplish some result, often one that is generalized or of frequent use; a computer program.

routing *n.* **1** In a communications network, the assignment and establishment of an active path between stations in the network. **2** The path so established.

routing indicator In the heading of a message, an address or group of characters that indicates the circuit or terminal to which the message is to be delivered.

row *n.* A group of characters, punches punching positions, etc., arranged in a horizontal sequence.

row binary On punched cards, a method of data representation in which adjacent positions in a row correspond to adjacent data bits.

row pitch The distance that separates corresponding points of adjacent rows.

RPG *abbr.* REPORT PROGRAM GENERATOR.

RS *abbr.* The RECORD SEPARATOR character.

RT *abbr.* REPERFORATOR/TRANSMITTER.

RTTY *abbr.* Radio teletypewriter communications.

rub-out character The DELETE CHARACTER.

ruly English An artificial form of English in which the mapping between words and concepts is exactly one-to-one, used by the U.S. Patent Office in the development of index codes.

run **1** *v.* To cause (a program or routine to be executed). **2** *n.* A single execution of a computer routine that proceeds in effect continuously although in a multiprogramming environment interrupts may have in fact occurred.

runaway *n.* A condition in which one of the parameters of a physical system undergoes a large, sudden, undesirable, and often destructive increase.

run book The collection of materials necessary for the documentation of a machine run.

running open In telegraphy, the condition of

a machine that is connected to an open or un-energized transmission line. A receiver de-codes this condition as the USASCII NULL CHARACTER and appears to be running.

S

sampling *n.* **1** The process of observing and/or recording the values of a function during discrete intervals of the independent variable or at discrete points, the intervals or points being regularly or irregularly spaced. **2** In statistics, the process of selecting a small group that is adequately representative of a larger population.

sampling theorem In information theory, a theorem stating that a continuous waveform $s(t)$ containing frequency components all of which are less than or equal to f cycles per second is unambiguously specified by a set of independent sample ordinates spaced no more than $1/2f$ second apart.

saturate *v.* To bring into a state of SATURATION.

saturation *n.* **1** A condition in which an increase in an independent variable will make little or no further change in the dependent variable. Thus magnetic saturation is the maximum magnetization of which a body is capable. **2** In colorimetry the degree to which a color is mixed with white; the more white, the lower the saturation.

scale *v.* To multiply (a quantity) by a chosen factor so that its range of variation is included within prescribed bounds.

scale factor The number by which a quantity is multiplied in scaling.

scan *v.* To examine the parts of in sequence.

scanner *n.* One who or that which scans.

SCATS *abbr.* SEQUENTIALLY CONTROLLED AUTOMATIC TRANSMITTER START.

scatter loading A type of FETCH that has the capability of placing the CONTROL SECTIONS of a LOAD MODULE in noncontiguous areas of main storage.

scatter read A procedure in which a computer distributes items of data between different areas of storage as they are read from magnetic tape.

scheduled maintenance Maintenance that is planned in advance and carried out in accordance with the plan.

scheduler *n.* **1** A JOB SCHEDULER. **2** A MASTER SCHEDULER.

scientific notation A form of floating-point notation in which the radix is ten.

search *v.* To subject (a set of items) to examination in order to locate those that have a desired property.

SEC *abbr.* Secant.

secant *n.* See TRIGONOMETRIC FUNCTIONS.

secondary storage AUXILIARY STORAGE.

second generation computer A computer whose electronic hardware is designed around solid-state components other than integrated circuits.

sectional center A control center that connects primary centers; a class 2 office.

seek *v.* To position the access mechanism of a direct access device at a specified location.

segment 1 *v.* To partition (a computer program) in such a way that its execution does not depend on its being in internal storage in its entirety at any one time. **2** *n.* Any of the divisions resulting from such a partition.

segregating unit A punched-card machine capable of selecting individual cards from a group.

select *v.* In logic and switching theory, to assume (one of a number of possible output states) dependent on input conditions.

selection *n.* The process of addressing a terminal and/or a component on a selective calling circuit.

selection check In the execution of an instruction, a check designed to ensure that the proper devices have been chosen.

selective calling The ability of a transmission station to direct a message to a specific one of several stations connected to the same line.

selective dump A DUMP of specified areas of storage.

selector *n.* A device that routes electrical pulses onto one or another of a pair of lines depending on the presence or absence of a control pulse.

self-adapting Indicating or relating to a system that can change its performance characteristics in response to information received from its environment.

self-checking code An ERROR-DETECTING CODE.

self-organizing Indicating or relating to a system that has the capability of affecting or determining its own internal structure.

semantics *n.* The study of the relations between signs and symbols and the things that they denote.

semiautomatic message switching center A center at which messages are routed by an operator on the basis of information which they contain.

sense switch An ALTERATION SWITCH.

sensitivity *n.* RESOLUTION.

sentence *n.* A sequence of COBOL statements terminated by a period.

sentinel *n.* A FLAG.

separator *n.* **1** An INFORMATION SEPARATOR. **2** A DELIMITER.

sequence *n.* A set of items or quantities ordered in such a way that the set maps onto the positive integers (or some contiguous subset thereof) in a one-to-one manner.

sequencer *n.* A punched card machine that places cards in a sequence that is based on the data they contain.

sequencing *n.* The ordering of the elements of a set according to some criterion such as rank or time.

sequential *adj.* Of, indicating, or relating to a sequence.

sequential computer A computer in which events occur one after another with little or no overlap.

sequential control A mode of computer operation in which instructions are executed in a defined sequence unless the sequence is explicitly altered by means of a JUMP.

sequential logic element A device having at

least one output channel and at least one input channel, all the channels having discrete states and operating in such a way that the condition(s) of the output channel(s) is a function of the previous condition(s) of the input channel(s).

Sequentially Controlled Automatic Transmitter Start A single-service multipoint teletypewriter arrangement that provides for transmission between all stations connected to a network without contention between stations.

Sequentially Operated Teletypewriter Universal Selector In 81D1 Automatic Teletypewriter Systems, the selecting device at each station, that is, a station control device at each Model 19 type station on a line.

sequential operation Indicating a device or system in which operations are performed in sequence.

sequential scheduling system A form of job scheduler that recognizes and executes job steps singly and in the sequence in which they appear in the input job stream.

serial *adj.* **1** Of or having to do with a series. **2** Of or indicating a device or system in which similar or related activities are performed in sequence by the same facility or facilities. **3** Indicating a computer in which individual parts of a word are processed in sequence by the same hardware.

serial access **1** Of or indicating sequential transfer of data in or out of storage. **2** Indicating the sequential execution of a set of processes. **3** Indicating the sequential processing of the individual parts of a data item, the same facilities being used repetitively for the various parts.

serial addition An addition process in which the corresponding digit pairs of the numbers added are processed individually beginning with the low-order digits, carries, in general, being propagated as they occur.

serial computer **1** A computer that carries on at least one of its basic functions, such as arithmetic, the handling of the component bits of a word, etc., in serial fashion. **2** A computer that contains just one arithmetic and logic unit.

serialize *v.* To change from operation or treatment that is parallel with respect to bits to treatment or operation that is serial with respect to bits.

serially reusable routine A routine in main storage that is available for use by another task after conclusion of its current use.

serial operations Indicating the sequential performance of a set of operations by means of the same hardware.

serial-parallel Indicating a computer that is partially serial and partially parallel.

serial processing Indicating the consecutive or sequential performance of a set of processes, the same hardware being used in each case.

serial transfer A transfer of data in which elements are sequentially transferred over a single line.

serial transmission In telecommunications, the transmission of successive groups of elements of the same signal in time intervals that follow one another (not necessarily contiguously) without overlap.

series *n.* In mathematics, the sum of a set of terms, the set being either finite or infinite and ordered. It can be shown, for example, that $e^x = 1 + x + x^2/2! + x^3/3! \ldots + x^n/n! + \ldots$ In a case where a function is validly represented by a series, it is relatively easy to compute the function to any desired degree of precision by means of a computer.

service *n.* The function, on the part of a communications common-carrier, of satisfying a customer's communications requirements.

service routine Any of various routines designed to generally facilitate the operation of a digital computer, as input/output or diagnostic routines.

servo *n.* A SERVOMECHANISM.

servomechanism *n.* **1** A FEEDBACK CONTROL SYSTEM in which at least one of the controlled variables is position, velocity, or acceleration. **2** Loosely, any feedback control system.

set **1** *n.* Any collection of items or elements. **2** *v.* To cause a storage device to take on a specified state, generally the state that represents 1 or something other than 0 or blank.

set theory The mathematical discipline that deals with the nature of and relations between sets.

setup *n.* A configuration of hardware or data necessary for the solution of a particular problem.

setup diagram A diagram that describes a particular SETUP.

several-for-one Indicating a macro instruction or a similar expression that has the property of allowing one statement in a source language to generate a number of instructions in the object language.

sexadecimal *adj.* HEXADECIMAL.

Shannon's capacity theorem In information theory, a theorem stating that it is possible to encode a source of messages having an information rate H bits/sec so that its information can be transmitted through a noisy channel with an arbitrarily small frequency of errors, provided that $H \leq C$ bits/sec, where C is called the limiting capacity of the channel. This rate C is known for only a few special cases. For a continuous input signal and additive Gaussian noise C is given by Shannon's formula, namely

$$C = B \log_2 (1 + M) \text{ bits/sec,}$$

where B is the signal bandwidth and M the signal-to-noise ratio. For a digital channel whose input consists of a source of equiprobable binary digits the capacity is given by

$$C = 1 + p \log_2 p + (1 - p) \log_2 (1 - p)$$

where p is the probability the output differs from the input, which can, in turn, be related to the SIGNAL-TO-NOISE RATIO.

shared file A direct access device which two systems may use at the same time.

sharing *n.* TIME SHARING.

sheffer stroke The logic operator NAND.

shift **1** *v.* To move (data) to the right or left with respect to the digit positions of a register or storage location. **2** *n.* The operation of shifting. See ARITHMETIC SHIFT; CYCLIC SHIFT; LOGIC SHIFT.

shift-in character A code extension character that can be used alone to reverse the effect of a SHIFT-OUT CHARACTER.

shift out To move (a digit or digits) out of a register by means of a SHIFT, the digit or digits so moved being in general lost.

shift-out character A code extension character that can be used alone to cause another character set to be substituted for the standard one, generally in order to allow the use of additional graphics.

shift register A register designed to allow its contents to be shifted. See SHIFT.

SI *abbr.* The SHIFT-IN CHARACTER.

sideband *n.* In the spectrum of a modulated carrier, any frequency other than the carrier frequency, that is, any of the frequencies that arise as a result of the process of MODULATION. It can be shown that a modulated carrier occupies a greater bandwidth than an unmodulated carrier and that, with certain exceptions, virtually all of this bandwidth must be transmitted for the signal to be successfully demodulated.

side circuit One of the circuits associated in the formation of a PHANTOM CHANNEL. For example, in a four-wire-a-circuit, the pair of wires that form the conductive path for the "go" signal form one side circuit while those that carry the "return" signal form the other.

side circuit loading coil A loading coil designed or intended to appear as an inductance in a side circuit with the minimum possible effect on the associated PHANTOM CHANNEL.

side circuit repeat coil A SIDE CIRCUIT REPEATING COIL.

side circuit repeating coil A repeating coil that functions as a transformer at a side circuit terminal and also as a means for superimposing one side of a PHANTOM CHANNEL on that circuit.

sight check A check in which the corresponding positions of two or more punched cards are superimposed and corresponding punches are verified by sight.

sign *n.* In mathematics, a PLUS SIGN or MINUS SIGN.

signal *n.* A physical event, generally the variation of one or more parameters of a flow of energy with respect to time, that carries information between points.

signal distance The corresponding digit positions which differ in a pair of binary words of the same length; for instance the words 10001 and 11010 have a signal distance of 3 (or 3 bits).

signal-to-noise ratio In a communications channel, the ratio of signal power to noise power, generally expressed in decibels.

sign bit A bit that occupies the SIGN POSITION of a numeral.

sign digit A digit located in the SIGN POSITION of a numeral.

signed field A FIELD that contains a character which indicates its algebraic sign.

significance *n.* In POSITIONAL REPRESENTATION, the multiplier associated with each of the digit positions.

significant *adj.* In statistics, designating a correlation or deviation whose probability of resulting from sampling errors or fluctuations is virtually negligible.

significant digit A digit that contributes to the meaning of a numeral and whose retention is necessary to preserve a given order of precision. It should be noted that when a calculation is performed the result can contain no more significant digits than that one of the operands which contains the least number of significant digits. Orders of magnitude must be considered, as the addition of 1.3×10^6 and 4.7×10^{-3} is meaningless as the uncertainty in the larger number far exceeds the magnitude of the smaller.

sign position A defined position in a numeral, generally at one end, such that the digit it contains is interpreted as an indication of the algebraic sign of the number represented.

simple buffering A technique of buffer control in which a buffer is assigned to a single data block, the assignment being terminated only upon closure of the data block.

simple name The rightmost component of a qualified name, as, for instance *man* in *primate · biped · man.*

simplex circuit A circuit superimposed on an existing two-wire circuit by means of center-tapped repeating coils, the superimposed

SIMPLEX CIRCUIT

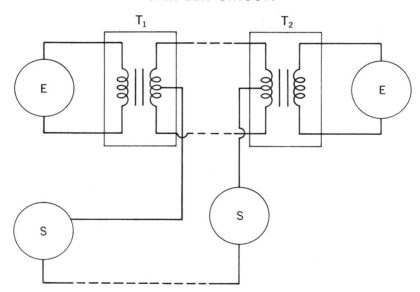

E terminals of existing circuit
S terminals of superimposed circuit
T₁, T₂ repeating coils

For more detailed explanation, see diagram at phantom circuit

circuit requiring an additional conductor to complete it.

simplex mode The mode of operation characteristic of a communications channel over which information can proceed in one direction only.

simulate *n.* To construct or arrange an easily observable system whose behavior represents certain features of or is analogous to the behavior of (a physical or abstract system) that is less readily observable.

simulation *n.* The process of simulating.

simulator *n.* **1** A device, system, or computer program used to SIMULATE some system that is of interest. **2** An EMULATOR.

simultaneous *adj.* Indicating or relating to two or more events that occur at the same instant of time.

simultaneous computer A computer, generally of an analog or hybrid variety, in which a computation is divided into parts such that a different element of hardware is used to perform each part, the interconnection of the various hardware units depending on the particular computation to be made.

simultaneous equations A set composed of two or more equations (to which there may or may not be a common solution) the conditions implied by each of the equations being imposed on all the variables at once.

sin *abbr.* Sine.

sine *n.* See TRIGONOMETRIC FUNCTIONS.

sine-cosine potentiometer A special potentiometer having two sliding taps and a specially tapered resistance element arranged so that the voltage between one sliding tap and ground is proportional to the sine of the shaft rotation and that between the other and ground is proportional to the cosine of the shaft rotation, often used as a RESOLVER and in ANALOG COMPUTERS.

sine wave A wave described by $f(t)$ where

$$f(t) = A \sin(\omega t + \phi).$$

It can be shown that $f(t)$ when formulated in this way includes all linear combinations of $\sin \omega t$ and $\cos \omega t$, dependent only on the values of A and ϕ.

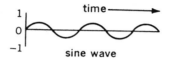

sine wave

singing *n.* A sound that results from oscillations that may occur on an unstable transmission system.

single-address Of or indicating an address format in which there is just one address part.

single-address message A message having one and only one intended destination.

single column punch A coding method in which any of the values 0 through 11 is represented by a single punch in a card column.

single-line repeater A telegraph repeater that consists of a pair of cross-coupled polar relays connected in series with the line.

single-office exchange An exchange served by a single central office.

single operation Somewhat loosely, HALF-DUPLEX.

single-precision Indicating a quantity or number that is represented by a single machine WORD. Compare DOUBLE PRECISION.

single-sideband transmission A form of carrier transmission in which either the set of sidebands above the carrier in frequency or below the carrier in frequency is suppressed, the carrier often being suppressed as well.

single step Indicating a method of computer operation in which each process or task is divided into a number of steps, each step being initiated by a single manual operation.

single-wire line A transmission line in which the actual ground acts as one side of the circuit. In this case *ground* refers to the earth itself and not just the point of nominal zero potential in the circuit.

sinusoid *n.* A SINE WAVE.

sinusoidal *adj.* Having the form of a SINE WAVE.

skeletal coding A form of coding in which some addresses and various other instruction parts remain unspecified. The missing parts are normally supplied by routines that adjust them in accordance with given parameters.

skew *n.* The angular displacement of a printed character, group of characters, or the like from a correct or intended position in a data format.

skip *v.* To suppress the execution of (one or more instructions) in some sequence of instructions.

slice **1** *n.* Those segments of a waveform that lie between a pair of specified amplitude limits on the same side of the zero axis. **2** To take a slice of (a waveform).

slicer *n.* A device that effectively amplifies a SLICE.

SLT *abbr.* SOLID LOGIC TECHNOLOGY.

smooth *v.* **1** To remove or reduce unwanted high-frequency components of (a waveform). **2** To reduce or remove unwanted high-frequency fluctuations of (data).

smoothline *n.* A NONLOADED LINE.

smudge *n.* In optical character recognition, the displacement of ink beyond the original or intended boundaries of a printed character as a result of shear effects.

S/N *abbr.* SIGNAL-TO-NOISE RATIO.

snapshot dump A dynamic DUMP performed selectively at chosen points in a machine run.

sneak current A current that leaks into a telephone circuit from some external source. While such currents are usually too small to cause immediate damage, they can have harmful long-term heating effects.

SNR *abbr.* SIGNAL-TO-NOISE RATIO.

SO *abbr.* The SHIFT-OUT CHARACTER.

software *n.* **1** Any of the specially prepared routines designed to optimize the operation of a digital computer installation. These include programmer aids such as assemblers, processors, library routines, and the like, and also more complex programs such as operating systems that to a large extent manage the entire installation. **2** Any of the manuals, circuit diagrams, logic diagrams, or other documents associated with a computer.

SOH *abbr.* The START OF HEADING CHARACTER.

solid logic technology The use of miniaturized solid-state modules in computers. Such modules have advantages in terms of reduced size and increased reliability, and, as a result of the shorter distances which currents must travel, faster circuitry.

solid state component An electronic component whose operation depends on electric or magnetic phenomena in solid, or in some cases amorphous, materials.

solid state computer A computer designed around solid state components; a SECOND-

GENERATION COMPUTER or THIRD GENERATION COMPUTER.

SOM *abbr.* START OF MESSAGE.

sonic delay line An ACOUSTIC DELAY LINE.

sort **1** *v.* To put (data or other items) into a sequence according to specified criteria. **2** *n.* The operation of sorting.

sorter *n.* One who or that which sorts.

SOTUS *abbr.* SEQUENTIALLY OPERATED TELE-TYPEWRITER UNIVERSAL SELECTOR.

sounder *n.* A telegraph transducer that produces an audible click at the beginning and end of each pulse of current, the operator being able to interpret the intervals between clicks as code elements and translate them into a message.

source language A language in which input is presented for translation into some other language.

source module A series of statements written in the source language of an assembler or compiler that constitutes the entire input to be processed in a single execution of the assembler or compiler.

source program A program written in a language such that it requires assembly or compilation before its execution is possible.

source recording The recording of data in a form that is directly accessible to machine reading, so as to allow its processing, transmission, or reuse without manual intervention.

SP *abbr.* The SPACE CHARACTER.

space **1** *n.* A signal condition that is the equivalent of a binary 0, often the absence of a current or a current that flows in the direction opposite to that interpreted as a MARK. **2** *n.* A defined unit of area, usually capable of accommodating a single character. **3** *n.* One or more SPACE CHARACTERS. **4** *v.* To cause the printing or display position to move in the nominal forward direction, generally downward or to the right, by a specified distance.

space character A character, a graphic which normally does not print, used to separate words or to cause the printing or display position to move one space in the nominal forward direction.

space-hold The normal condition of a transmission line on which there is no traffic, that is, the transmission of a steady SPACE, often a customer-selected option.

space suppression The inhibition of changes of printing of display position.

space-to-mark transition The transition from a signal condition that is interpreted as a SPACE to one that is interpreted as a MARK.

spacing bias BIAS DISTORTION.

special character Any of various graphic characters other than a letter, a digit, or a space character.

special purpose computer A computer designed especially to handle problems of a particular type.

specific address An ABSOLUTE ADDRESS.

specific coding ABSOLUTE CODING.

spectral response The variation in sensitivity of a photosensitive device as a function of the wavelength of the light incident upon it.

split *n.* A COLUMN SPLIT.

spool *n.* A REEL.

spot punch A device for making PUNCHES one at a time.

SPX circuit A SIMPLEX CIRCUIT.

squeezeout *n.* In optical character recognition, the displacement of ink from the centers to the edges of STROKES as a result of excessive pressure in printing.

SSC *abbr.* STATION SELECTION CODE.

stability *n.* **1** The degree to which a transmission system, amplifying system, or control system is able to resist conditions such as oscillation or runaway. **2** COMPUTATIONAL STABILITY. **3** LIGHT STABILITY.

stacked job processing A technique that permits multiple job definitions to be grouped (stacked) for presentation to the system, which automatically recognizes the jobs, one after the other. More advanced systems allow job definitions to be added to the group (stack) at any time and from any source, and, in addition, honor priorities.

stacker *n.* A CARD STACKER.

standard form NORMALIZED FORM.

standard test-tone power One milliwatt (0 dbm) at 1 khz.

standby *n.* **1** A condition in which a piece of equipment is inactive but capable of being returned to stable operation in a short time. **2** A secondary unit of equipment to be used in place of the primary unit should a failure occur.

standing-on-nines carry In parallel addition of decimal numbers, an arrangement whereby a carry signal to a given digit place is forwarded to the next higher order place if the sum in the given place is 9 at that time.

start element In certain serial transmissions, the first element of a character, used to permit synchronization.

start of heading character A communication control character used to initiate a message heading.

start of message A character or group of char-

acters transmitted by a polled terminal, indicating to other stations on the line that the data following indicates the addresses of stations on the line which are to receive the answering message.

start of text character A communication control character that terminates a heading and marks the beginning of the actual text.

start pulse In Baudot teletypewriter code, a space pulse transmitted just ahead of the five bits representing each character as a START ELEMENT.

start-stop transmission Asynchronous transmission in which the receiving apparatus is prepared for each set of code elements corresponding to a character by the reception of a START ELEMENT and is restored to a resting state in preparation for the reception of the next character by a STOP ELEMENT.

statement *n.* An expression or generalized instruction written in a programming language.

static dump A DUMP executed at a particular point in a machine run, frequently at the end.

staticize *v.* To convert (data that is serial or otherwise time-dependent) into a form that is independent of time.

static storage Any storage that is not DYNAMIC STORAGE.

station *n.* **1** In a communications network, any of the points at which traffic can be originated or received. **2** A TAPE UNIT.

station arrangement In the terminology used in tariffs, a device somewhat analogous to a DATA SET required on certain subvoice-grade leased channels.

station battery The source of electric power that a station uses to generate signals.

station selection code In Western Union terminology, a signal which can be directed to an outlying telegraph receiver in order to activate its printer automatically.

step 1 *n*. In a computer routine, a single defined operation. 2 *v*. To cause the execution of a step by a computer. 3 *n*. A STEP FUNCTION.

stepping switch A switching device (essentially a relay) having *n* discrete conditions and which advances from one condition to the next each time it receives an input pulse.

step-by-step switch A STEPPING SWITCH.

step-by-step system A line-switching system that uses STEPPING SWITCHES.

step change A STEP-FUNCTION increment or decrement of a variable.

step function A function defined by the following equations:

$$f(t) = A, t_0 < t; f(t) = B, t > t_0,$$

where *A*, *B* are constants. The unit step function $U(t)$ appears often in the analysis of physical systems. For $U(t) A = 0, t_0 = 0, B = 1$. Like any discontinuous function the unit step is undefined at the point of discontinuity. See DELTA FUNCTION. As it is possible to approximate any function by a sum of step functions, the response of a system to a step function is a convenient generalization of its behavior.

stochastic variable A variable that has a probability p_i with which it may assume each of its possible values x_i.

stop bit A STOP ELEMENT.

stop element In asynchronous serial transmissions, an element placed at the end of a code sequence representing a character in order to ensure recognition of the next START ELEMENT.

stop instruction A machine operation or routine which causes the machine to require

manual action other than the pressing of the start key in order for processing to continue.

stop pulse In Baudot teletypewriter code, a MARK pulse used as a STOP ELEMENT.

stop time The time required for a tape transport mechanism to come to a complete stop at the end of a read or write operation.

storage *n*. A device or array of devices capable of accepting data and holding it and from which the data can be retrieved at a later time.

storage allocation The use or reservation of specified blocks of storage by or for specified blocks of data.

storage block An area consisting of 2084 contiguous bytes of main storage to which a storage key can be assigned.

storage capacity The amount of data that a STORAGE can accommodate.

storage cell Any of the basic units of a storage, as, for instance, a BINARY CELL.

storage device A device that functions as part or all of a STORAGE.

storage key An indicator associated with one or more storage blocks in such a way that a task must have a matching protection key in order to make use of the block or blocks.

storage protection An arrangement by means of which access to storage blocks can be restricted with respect to reading, writing, or both.

storage register A device designed to store a unit of data, generally one or two WORDS.

store 1 *v*. To put (data) into a storage. 2 *v*. To hold (data), as in a storage. 3 *n*. A STORAGE.

store and forward In data communications, a process in which a flow of data is interrupted in such a way that the data is stored at some location between the sender and receiver and forwarded to the receiver at a later time.

stored program computer A computer in which the sequence of instructions that control it is stored internally in such a way that it is indistinguishable from stored data except by conventions and rules. It is thus possible for a computer of this type to operate upon its own instructions as though they were data and, in cases of programmer mistakes, to interpret stored data as instructions.

STR *abbr.* SYNCHRONOUS TRANSMITTER RECEIVER.

straight line coding A form of coding in which a sequence of instructions that is reused by the program is literally repeated rather than being reentered by means of a LOOP.

string *n.* A set of entities that form a sequence.

striping *n.* In flowcharting, the placement of a line across the upper part of a symbol as an indication that the process it represents is described in greater detail elsewhere in the same flowchart set.

stroke *n.* In character recognition, a line segment or a segment of an arc that is used as part of a graphic character.

stroke centerline In character recognition, a line equidistant from the two edges of a STROKE.

stroke edge In character recognition, the boundary between a side of a stroke and the background. In defining such a boundary it is necessary to average out the irregularities that arise as a result of the printing and detection processes.

stroke width In character recognition, the distance between the stroke edges, measured perpendicular to the stroke centerline.

stunt box A device that controls the nonprinting functions of a teletypewriter terminal, as carriage return, line feed, etc., and recognizes line control characters.

STX *abbr.* The START OF TEXT CHARACTER.

SUB *abbr.* The SUBSTITUTE CHARACTER.

subalphabet *n.* Any subset of an alphabet.

subcarrier *n.* A modulated CARRIER which is itself used as modulating information imposed on another carrier.

subchannel *n.* A communications channel derived from another channel and occupying only a part of its information-bearing capacity, as in time-division or frequency-division multiplexing.

subcycle generator In a telephone system, a circuit that reduces the frequency of the ringing current to a submultiple to provide selective ringing for customers that share a line.

submultiple ringer A SUBCYCLE GENERATOR.

subprogram *n.* A MODULE.

subroutine *n.* A routine that can be incorporated into another routine.

subroutine call In object coding, a subroutine that determines when the source program has called for a subroutine, identifies the routine called for, and causes it to be identified in the object code.

subscriber's drop The line that extends from a telephone cable to a subscriber's premises.

subset *n.* **1** In set theory, a set that has all of its elements contained in another set. **2** In communications, the transmitting and receiving apparatus located on the subscriber's premises, as, for example, a telephone. **3** A device that performs modulation and demodulation.

substitute character An accuracy control character used as a replacement for a character that has been determined to be invalid, erroneous, or nonrepresentable on a particular device.

substitute mode A mode of transmission used with exchange buffering on which segments are pointed to and exchanged with user work areas.

substrate *n.* The supporting material for a microelectronic device such as an integrated circuit, often used as a part of the circuit or device.

subsystem A system that is itself a component of a larger system.

subtask *n.* A task that another task creates by means of the attach macro instruction.

subtract *v.* **1** To perform SUBTRACTION. **2** To add the additive inverse of (a number) to another number.

subtraction *n.* To determine the sum that is formed when the additive inverse of a number is added to another number, that is, the determination of the sum $x = a + (-b)$.

subtrahend *n.* In SUBTRACTION, the number whose additive inverse is added to another.

subvoice-grade channel A communications channel (normally with telegraph channels excluded from this definition by convention) whose bandwidth is too small to accommodate voice transmissions, usually a subchannel derived from a voice-grade channel.

sum *n.* The number that results when a set of numbers is added.

summary punch **1** A card-punching machine that can be connected to an accounting machine to punch totals on balance cards. **2** To punch summary information onto cards.

summation check A checking procedure in which the digits of a numeral are added and the sum compared, usually, with a previously computed value.

superimposed ringing SUPERPOSED RINGING.

superposed circuit A channel derived from the circuits intended to serve other channels in such a way that the interaction between the original channels and the derived channel is negligible. See PHANTOM CHANNEL.

superposed ringing A technique in which alternating currents and direct currents of both polarities are combined for use as ringing currents in order to provide selective ringing for subscribers sharing a line.

supervisor *n.***1** A routine by means of which the use of system resources is coordinated and by means of which the flow of operations through the central processing unit is maintained; an executive routine. **2** An OVERLAY SUPERVISOR.

supervisory relay In a telephone system, a relay which during a call is controlled by the transmitter current supplied to a subscriber line and which accepts signals from associated stations that control actions on the part of operators or switching mechanisms.

supervisory routine An EXECUTIVE ROUTINE.

supervisory signals Signals that indicate the various operating conditions of circuit combinations.

suppressed carrier transmission A method of transmission in which the carrier of a modulated signal is reduced in strength or eliminated virtually entirely, one or both of the sidebands (the signal components that actually represent information) being transmitted.

suppression *n.* ZERO SUPPRESSION.

switch **1** *n.* A circuit element (especially one that is mechanical in nature) having two conditions, one in which its impedance is virtually zero, and another in which its impedance is virtually infinite. Switches are often arranged so that many are actuated by a single control. **2** *v.* To control or select by means of a switch. **3** *v.* To change from one state to another.

switchboard *n.* A panel or arrangement of panels bearing switches for connecting and disconnecting electric circuits.

switch hook On a telephone set, a switch that operates when the receiver is removed from or replaced onto the hook.

switching algebra BOOLEAN ALGEBRA, when applied to switching circuits, digital systems, etc.

switching center A location at which a large number of circuits terminate and at which interconnections can be made or traffic transferred between them.

switching pad An attenuator that is automatically switched in or out of a circuit as required.

switching theory The theory dealing with circuit elements that have two or more discrete states; the theory of digital systems.

switch room In a telephone central office building, the area in which the switching mechanism and associated apparatus are housed.

switch train In telephony, the sequence of switches required to establish a connection between a calling station and a called station.

symbol *n.* Anything that by means of relationship, association, or convention represents something other than itself.

symbolic address A label attached to a word or statement so that the programmer can conveniently refer to it without knowledge of its actual storage location.

symbolic logic A mathematical discipline that studies the relations of formal logic by means of special symbols, the purpose of the symbols being to avoid the ambiguities and inadequacies inherent in natural languages.

symbol rank DIGIT PLACE.

symbol string A STRING composed of symbols and only symbols.

symbol table A table that indicates a mapping between two sets of symbols.

SYN *abbr.* The SYNCHRONOUS IDLE CHARACTER.

sync *n.* SYNCHRONIZATION.

synchronism *n.* SYNCHRONIZATION.

synchronization *n.* **1** A condition in which if there are two sequences of events, say the ordered sets *A* and *A'* such that for every event *a* in *A*, there is a corresponding event *a'* in *A'*, every event *a'* occurs a uniform time after *a*. **2** The process of bringing two or more systems into such a condition.

synchronization pulses Pulses sent to a receiving apparatus by a transmitter to keep the two operating in synchronism.

synchronize *v.* To cause (two or more systems or subsystems) to operate in or come into synchronization.

synchronous *adj.* Occurring concurrently, and with a regular or predictable time relationship; synchronized.

synchronous computer A computer in which all basic operations can be initiated only if a timing pulse, usually locally generated, is present, any sequence of operations normally being performed in synchronism with the timing pulses.

synchronous idle character In a synchronous data transmission system, a control character transmitted in the absence of other traffic in order to maintain or achieve synchronism between the apparatus at the various data terminals.

synchronous transmission Transmission in which the sending and receiving apparatus are caused to operate in synchronism.

synchronous transmitter receiver In IBM data terminals that use synchronous transmission, the unit that transmits and receives data and control information and maintains line synchronization.

sync pulse A SYNCHRONIZATION PULSE.

syntax *n.* **1** The arrangements and interrelations of the elements of a language. **2** The set of rules that defines these arrangements and interrelations.

synthesis *n.* The assembly of a unit from a set of separate or subordinate parts.

synthetic language An ARTIFICIAL LANGUAGE.

system *n.* **1** An entity composed of all the hardware, personnel, methods, and the like, necessary to the accomplishment of some defined function or functions. **2** A group of components interconnected so as to perform a specific function. **3** A set of interacting physical entities: a *system* of particles.

system input unit A device specified as a source of an input job stream.

system library The collection of all catalogued data sets at an installation.

system macro instruction A predefined macro instruction by means of which access to operating system facilities is provided.

system output unit An output unit shared by all jobs, onto which specified output data is transcribed.

system residence volume The volume (def. 1) that contains the nucleus of the operating system and the highest-level index of the catalog.

systems analysis The analysis of an activity to determine exactly what must be done in order that it be carried on in optimum fashion.

systems checks A check on overall system operation, either by built-in mechanisms or by means of software.

T

table *n.* A collection in which each item is uniquely identified, as by means of a label, its position, or the like.

table look-up **1** A procedure in which the value of a function for various values of its independent variable are obtained from a table. **2** A procedure in which the results of various arithmetic operations are obtained from a table.

tabulate *v.* **1** To arrange (data) in the form of a table. **2** To accumulate several separate totals at the same time.

tag *n.* A set of characters affixed to a data item for identification; a label.

tandem office A telephone office that makes connections between local end offices over tandem trunks in an area where the exchanges are so densely concentrated that direct interconnection of all end offices is uneconomical. The tandem office completes all connections between end offices but is not directly connected to subscribers.

tape *n.* **1** MAGNETIC TAPE. **2** PAPER TAPE.

tape-controlled carriage An automatic paper-feeding carriage controlled by a punched paper tape.

tape deck A TAPE UNIT.

tape drive A mechanism that carries a magnetic or paper tape past one or more heads with which it is kept in contact for reading or writing.

tape editor A support routine designed for use in the editing, updating, and correction of programs that are contained on tape.

tape operating system An OPERATING SYSTEM which, except for the segment that is always in main storage, is stored on magnetic tape.

tape relay A method of relaying messages between stations using perforated tape as the intermediate storage medium.

tape skip An instruction that causes a portion of a tape to be erased and skipped over when some defect in the tape itself causes a write error that persists through several trials.

tape station A TAPE UNIT.

tape-to-card Indicating apparatus or techniques for transferring data from a tape, magnetic or paper, to punched cards.

tape transport A TAPE DRIVE.

tape unit A device consisting of a tape drive, the heads necessary for reading and writing, and associated controls.

target language OBJECT LANGUAGE.

target program OBJECT PROGRAM.

target set In a mapping operation, the set into or onto which the mapping is done.

tariff *n.* **1** The published rate at which a communications common carrier charges for a particular service or for the use of some facility. **2** The vehicle by means of which a regulatory agency may approve or disapprove of some such service, facility, or charge.

task *n.* A unit of work for the central processor from the standpoint of the control program, thus the basic multiprogramming unit with respect to the control program.

task control block The accumulation of control data relating to a particular task.

task dispatcher The control program function that selects from the task queue the next task to be processed and gives it control of the central processor.

task management The functions of the control program that regulate the use of system resources other than input/output devices by tasks.

task queue The queue that contains all the task control blocks that are in the system at any one time.

TD *abbr.* TRANSMITTER-DISTRIBUTOR.

tele-autograph A telegraph instrument in which the movements of a pen in a transmitting apparatus are transformed into electrical signals which in turn cause a pen in the receiver to duplicate the movements of the pen in the transmitter. The electrical signals represent, in effect, the instantaneous coordinates of the transmitting pen.

telecommunication *n.* The transmission of information between widely separated locations by means of electrical or electromagnetic systems such as telegraph, radio, or the like.

telecommunications *n.* The branch of science and technology that deals with the transmission of information over long distances by electrical or electromagnetic means.

telegraph *n.* A system of telecommunication in which messages are coded and transmitted as pulses of electrical or electromagnetic energy.

telegraph grade circuit A circuit in which the maximum signalling rate is 75 bauds, generally considered sufficient for teletypewriter transmission.

telemeter *v.* To measure (physical parameters) and transmit the data so obtained to a remote location by means of telecommunication.

telemetry *n.* The techniques and technology used in telemetering.

telephone *n.* 1 A telecommunications system designed principally for voice transmissions. 2 The basic transmitting-receiving equipment provided to a telephone company subscriber for use in voice communications.

telephone company A communications common carrier that provides public telephone service.

teleprinter *n.* The equipment used in a printing telegraph system. See TELETYPEWRITER.

teleprocessing *n.* The use of communications facilities in a data-processing system.

TELESPEED The marketing term used by Western Union for equipment comparable to DATASPEED.

Teletype Any of various items of teleprinter equipment used in communications systems: a trademark of the Teletype Corporation.

teletypewriter *n.* 1 Any of various items of teleprinter equipment. 2 The basic equipment made by the Teletype Corporation.

Teletypewriter Exchange Service A public switched teletypewriter service offered by American Telephone & Telegraph, in which suitably equipped teletypewriter stations are connected to a central office and provided with access to other such stations in the United States and Canada.

teletypewriter switching systems Total message switching systems in which the terminals are TELEPRINTER equipment.

telewriter *n.* A TELE-AUTOGRAPH.

Telex A Western Union term for a service that is similar to the Teletypewriter Exchange Service provided by American Telephone & Telegraph, but which extends worldwide.

temporary storage Storage locations that are used only for intermediate results.

tens complement In decimal notation, the radix COMPLEMENT.

terminal *n.* In a communications network, any apparatus that is capable of transmitting or receiving information.

terminal repeater A REPEATER designed for use at the end of a trunk line.

terminal room In a telephone central office, private branch exchange, or private exchange, a room which contains all such equipment as distributing frames and relays except for that mounted in the switchboard sections.

terminated line A transmission line that works into a remote-end load equal to its CHARACTERISTIC IMPEDANCE.

ternary *adj.* 1 Indicating a condition, selection, etc., in which there are three and only three distinct possibilities. 2 Indicating a system of numeration in which 3 (notated 10 in the system) is the RADIX.

ternary incremental representation A form of INCREMENTAL REPRESENTATION in which each increment can be plus one quantum, minus one quantum, or zero.

test board A switchboard equipped with test apparatus, so designed that it can be connected to telephone lines or central office equipment.

TESTRAN TEST TRANSLATOR.

test tone An audio-frequency signal introduced into a circuit for purposes of identification or adjustment, or in order to locate malfunctions.

Test translator A facility by means of which various debugging procedures can be specified in assembler language programs.

tetrad *n.* A group of four, in particular, a group of four pulses used to represent a number in decimal or hexadecimal notation.

TEX *abbr.* TELEX.

text *n.* **1** In communications and USASCII, a sequence of characters defined as an entity by being preceded and terminated by one STX control character and one EXT control character, respectively. **2** In an object module or load module, the control sections.

thin film A layer of material that is one to several molecules thick.

third generation computer A computer designed around SOLID LOGIC TECHNOLOGY.

three-address Indicating an instruction format in which there are three address parts.

three-plus-one address Indicating an instruction that contains three operand addresses and a control address.

three-row keyboard The keyboard used on Baudot-coded teletypewriter equipment. Compare FOUR-R W KEYBOARD.

threshold *n.* **1** A logic operator having the property that if P is a set of m statements p_i, and x is a statement defined as equivalent to threshold P, then x is true if and only if at least n of the m statements in P are true, m being a nonnegative integer, n being a specified nonnegative integer, and $n \leq m$. **2** The nonnegative integer n in def. 1.

threshold element A device that implements the logic operator THRESHOLD and has the additional property that each of the statements p_i in P can be weighted, that is, each of the statements p_i may have associated with it a positive integer w_i that indicates the number of times it appears in P, it being understood that all the statements identical with any p_i are all true or false together at any one time.

throughput *n.* A figure of merit for a system indicating the rate at which it can handle data.

tie line A private line of a type provided by communications common carriers used to link two or more points.

tie trunk A telephone line or channel that connects two branch exchanges directly.

time base A known and precisely controlled function of time by which some process or phenomenon is controlled or measured.

time base generator A device used to produce a time base, as, for example, a CLOCK.

time-derived channel An additional channel obtained by the application of TIME-DIVISION MULTIPLEX to another channel.

time-division multiplex A method in which several messages are transmitted through a single communications channel by sampling the messages in sequence and transmitting the samples in nonoverlapping time intervals. This method is related to FREQUENCY-DIVISION MULTIPLEX in the sense that the number of time intervals that can be unambiguously specified in the channel is a function of its bandwidth. See SAMPLING THEOREM.

time-of-day clock A device that indicates the

actual time through a 24-hour period accurate to 0.1 second, its reading being available to the central processor upon demand.

time-out The interval of time provided for the occurrence of certain operations, such as response to polling or addressing, before system operation is interrupted and must be restarted.

time-share To use (a device or system) in a way somewhat analogous to the use of a communications channel in TIME-DIVISION MULTIPLEX, that is, in such a way that the device divides its time into nonoverlapping intervals and devotes successive intervals to different operations. Normally the speed of operation of the device is sufficiently high and the time intervals sufficiently short that it would appear to an observer that all the operations are being done simultaneously.

time slicing See TIME SHARE.

time-switching multiplex TIME-DIVISION MULTIPLEX.

tip *n.* In a manual switchboard, the end of a plug used to make circuit connections, normally connected to the positive terminal of the battery that energizes the circuit.

tip side The side of a communications circuit that is connected to the positive terminal of the energizing battery.

TLU *abbr.* Table look-up.

toggle *n.* **1** A FLIP-FLOP. **2** Any BISTABLE device.

toll *n.* In public switched systems, a charge imposed for making connections outside of an exchange, based on the distance over which the connection is made and the time for which it is maintained.

toll center A central office at which channels and toll message circuits terminate; a class 4 office.

toll-free number An ENTERPRISE NUMBER.

tone *n.* In communications, an audio-frequency signal.

tone dialing See PUSHBUTTON DIALING.

torn-tape switching center A location at which incoming printed and punched paper tape is manually detached and transferred to the proper outgoing circuit.

TOS *abbr.* TAPE OPERATING SYSTEM.

tracing routine A documentation routine that produces a record of certain events in the course of execution of a program.

track *n.* On a moving storage medium, the sequence of storage locations that is accessible from a given read head position.

track pitch The distance that separates the centers of a pair of tracks.

traffic *n.* The signals or information that pass through a communications system.

trailer record A record that follows one or more records and contains data related to that contained in the record or records.

train *n.* The sequence of hardware units that are connected together in order to forward or complete a call.

TRAN *abbr.* TRANSMIT.

transacter *n.* A system of data collection that allows source data to be entered at a remote station, transmitted to the data-processing center, and translated into machine-sensible form.

transaction data Data that is current, that is, data that results from new events or transactions.

transaction file A file of current or relatively transient data used to update a master file or to be processed with reference to data contained in a master file.

transceiver *n.* A terminal that has the capability of both transmitting and receiving.

transcribe *v.* To copy (the data contained in one external storage medium) into another external storage medium.

transducer *n.* A device whose input and output energy are of different types, used to couple energy between systems.

transfer **1** *n.* A JUMP. **2** *v.* To TRANSMIT.

transfer card A transition CARD.

transfer check A check designed to ensure that data has been accurately transmitted and received.

transfer instruction A JUMP.

transfer-of-control card A TRANSITION card.

transform *v.* To change (data) from one form to another according to a set of unambiguous rules.

transformer *n.* A device for transferring ac current from one circuit to another by means of magnetic induction. Each circuit is represented by a winding around a magnetic core, the ratio of the voltages in the two circuits being (in an ideal transformer) equal to the ratio of the number of turns. The product of current and voltage is, except for losses, the same in both circuits.

transient *n.* Any nonrepetitive WAVEFORM.

transistor *n.* An active three-terminal semiconductor device in which the current between one pair of terminals is a function of the current between the other pair. A transistor can be used for switching or linear amplification much in the manner of a vacuum tube but with great savings in size and operating power.

transition *n.* The passage of a switching device from one of its possible conditions to another.

transition card In a computer that is capable of accepting a program via a card reader, a card that indicates that the entire program has been loaded and execution is to begin.

translate *v.* **1** To change the representation of (a corpus of information) from one language or form into another. **2** To move an object, reference point, or coordinate system in space. **3** To move (an electrical signal) to a different BAND.

translator *n.* One who or that which translates, in particular, a device or routine.

transliterate *v.* To represent or, often, approximate the characters of one alphabet by means of appropriate characters or combinations of characters in another.

transmission *n.* **1** The sending of information from one location to another, generally by electrical means. **2** The information or message thus sent. **3** In communications and USASCII, a series of transmitted characters, headings and texts being included.

transmission level RELATIVE TRANSMISSION LEVEL.

transmit data lead One of the basic data set leads defined in EIA standard RS–232–B.

transmittal mode The method by which the contents of an input buffer are made available to the program and by which a program makes records available for output.

transmitter-distributor In a teletypewriter terminal, especially in modern usage, one that uses a paper tape transmitter, a device that opens and closes the line circuit in timed sequence.

transmitter start code In the terminology of the Bell System, a sequence of characters that when transmitted to a remote teletype-writer terminal automatically polls its tape transmitter or keyboard.

transport *n.* A TAPE TRANSPORT.

transposition *n.* In telecommunications, the interchange of the positions of the conductors of open-wire lines in such a way that any spurious signals that are induced in the line tend to cancel themselves out.

transverse crosstalk coupling The vector sum of the couplings between adjacent short lengths of a disturbed and a disturbing circuit, the effects of intermediate flow in other nearby circuits being disregarded.

trap *n.* A conditional jump to a prespecified location, activated by hardware independently of the program, the location from which the jump occurred being automatically recorded.

trapped instruction **1** An instruction that is executed by a software routine in cases where the necessary hardware is absent and in cases where the central processor is not in the state required. **2** An instruction whose execution is suppressed.

triad *n.* A group of three, in particular, a group composed of three bits or pulses.

trigger **1** *n.* An electronic device that upon receipt of a pulse that has at least a specified amplitude and duration produces an output pulse whose amplitude and duration are close controlled. **2** *n.* A pulse that causes a flip-flop to change states. **3** *v.* To actuate, as by means of a pulse.

trigonometric functions Certain functions of an angle or an arc, of which the most commonly used are the sine, cosine, tangent, cotangent, secant and cosecant. The following statements may be derived from definitions of the functions (see diagram) and the Pythagorean theorem:

$$\tan\theta = \frac{\sin\theta}{\cos\theta}, \sin\theta = \frac{1}{\csc\theta}, \cos\theta = \frac{1}{\sec\theta}, \tan\theta = \frac{1}{\operatorname{ctn}\theta}, \sin^2\theta + \cos^2\theta = 1, \tan^2\theta + 1 = \sec^2\theta, +1 = \csc^2\theta.$$

It can also be shown by other means that

$$e^{i\theta} = \cos\theta + i\sin\theta, \cos\theta = \frac{e^{i\theta} + e^{-i\theta}}{2},$$

$$\sin\theta = \frac{e^{i\theta} - e^{-i\theta}}{2i}, \sin-\theta = -\sin\theta, \cos-\theta = \cos\theta.$$

See HYPERBOLIC FUNCTIONS.

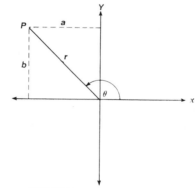

TRIGONOMETRIC FUNCTIONS
If θ is the angle formed by r and the x axis, and P is a point on r having a as its abscissa and b as its ordinate, then sine $\theta = b/r$, cosine $\theta = a/r$, tangent $\theta = b/a$, cosecant $\theta = r/b$, secant $\theta = r/a$, and cotangent $\theta = a/b$.

troubleshoot *v.* DEBUG.

trouble ticket In the use of telephone test-boards, a small form used to report any circuit condition that requires the attention of a technician who mans such a unit.

trouble unit A figure of merit applied to one or a combination of telephone circuits to indicate expected reliability over a specified period of time.

true complement A RADIX COMPLEMENT.

truncate v. 1 To terminate a computation that is intrinsically arbitrarily long when some condition or rule has been satisfied, as, for example, to compute π to a specified number of decimal places. 2 To drop one or more of the low-order digits of a number, as in normalization.

truncation error An error that arises as a result of TRUNCATION.

trunk n. In telephony, a channel between two control offices or switching centers that is used in providing subscriber connections.

trunk exchange An exchange whose primary purpose is the interconnection of trunks.

trunk hunting An arrangement in which an incoming call is switched to the next number in sequence if the original called number is busy.

truth table A table that expresses a logic function as a listing of all the possible combinations of the values of the independent (input) variables together with the value of the dependent (output) variable for each combination. (See illustration in opposite column.)

TSC abbr. TRANSMITTER START CODE.

TTY abbr. TELETYPEWRITER equipment.

tube n. A DISPLAY TUBE.

turing machine A mathematical model of a hypothetical device that, as a function of its present state, reads from, writes on, and moves an arbitrarily long tape, and changes its own internal state. A machine of this type is used as a model of computer-like behavior. See UNIVERSAL TURING MACHINE.

Truth table for
AND operator

A	B	A · B*
0	0	0
0	1	0
1	0	0
1	1	1

* A · B is symbolic notation for A **AND** B

turnaround time 1 The time that elapses between the submission of a job to a data-processing installation and the return of results. 2 On a half-duplex circuit, the time required to change over from sending to receiving or vice versa.

twelve punch A punch in the uppermost row of a card. See also Y-PUNCH.

twin check A checking procedure in which the same operations are performed by duplicate sets of hardware and the results automatically compared.

two-address Indicating an address format in which there are two address parts.

two-out-of-five code A positional notation in which each decimal digit is represented as a sequence of five binary digits no more than three of which are of the same kind, that is, of the five binary digits at most three are 0's and at most three are 1's.

two-plus-one address Indicating an instruction format in which there are two operand addresses and one control address.

twos complement In binary notation, the radix COMPLEMENT.

two-state variable A variable capable of assuming two and only two different states, generally notated as 0 and 1, a binary variable.

two-tone keying FREQUENCY-SHIFT KEYING.

two-wire circuit A circuit formed by a source feeding a pair of metallic conductors which are insulated one from the other and which, in turn, feed a load. A circuit of this kind can be used as a one-way transmission path, a half-duplex path, or a duplex path.

TWX *abbr.* TELETYPEWRITER EXCHANGE SERVICE.

typebar *n.* A linear type element that contains the complete set of characters printed in a particular application.

type font A complete set of type of a particular face and size.

typing reperforator A reperforator that types on chadless tape in such a way that each printed character is located about one-half inch past the punching to which it corresponds.

U

U format A data set format in which the lengths of the various blocks are unspecified or unknown.

ultrasonics *n.* The branch of science and technology that deals with acoustic phenomena whose frequencies lie above the range audible by human beings.

unary operation A MONADIC OPERATION.

unattended operation Those automatic features of the hardware of a terminal or system that permit signals or data to be handled without the intervention of a human operator.

unbalanced *adj.* Of or indicating an electrical transmission line or network in which the impedances measured from corresponding points on opposite sides are unequal. Compare BALANCED.

unconditional branch An UNCONDITIONAL JUMP.

unconditional jump A jump that occurs regardless of the internal state of the machine.

unconditional transfer An UNCONDITIONAL JUMP.

underflow *n.* **1** The production of a negative result whose magnitude is such that it exceeds the capacity of the register or storage location reserved for it. **2** That part of a result which is lost when such a condition occurs.

union *n.* In set theory, an operation having the property that if A is a set and B is a set, and C is a set equivalent to A union B, then C contains all the elements of A and all the elements of B, including such elements, if any, as are common to both sets. This operation is closely related to the logic operator OR. Compare INTERSECTION.

union catalog A merged listing of the contents of two or more libraries.

unipolar transmission NEUTRAL TRANSMISSION.

unit *n.* **1** A basic element, in particular, a module or device that has a special, defined function. **2** A quantity whose measure is defined as that of the smallest positive integer, that is to say, as 1: a *unit* distance; a *unit* mass.

uniterm *n.* In information retrieval, a word, symbol, or number used to identify a particular item.

uniterm system A type of COORDINATE INDEXING in which the descriptors are UNITERMS.

unit record **1** Any of a set of records all of which are similar in form and content. **2** A punched card. **3** Formerly, a punched card containing a single record.

unit separator A character designed for the demarcation of the logical boundary between items of data that are referred to as units.

unit step See STEP FUNCTION.

unit step function See STEP FUNCTION.

universal button box A set of pushbuttons whose conditions can be interrogated by a program.

universal interconnecting device A manually-actuated relay device that allows peripheral units to be interchanged without manual shifting of cables.

universal turing machine A generalized TURING MACHINE such that any conceivable turing machine can be shown to be one of its special cases.

unpack *v.* To restore (packed data) to its original form. See PACK.

update *v.* **1** To incorporate current information into a masterfile in accordance with some specified procedure. **2** To modify (an instruction) in such a way that each of its addresses is incremented by a specified amount at each execution.

uptime *n.* Time during which a piece of equipment is in proper operating condition. Compare DOWNTIME.

US In USASCII, the information separator used at the lowest level of hierarchy.

USASCII USA STANDARD CODE FOR INFORMATION INTERCHANGE.

USA Standard Code for Information Interchange A code that uses eight bits per character (one being a PARITY BIT), the character set consisting of graphic characters and control characters, used for the interchange of information between data-processing systems and communications systems, and between the equipment associated with systems of both types.

user *n.* One who uses the services provided by a computing system.

user's set In a communication or signaling system, equipment located on the premises of a user and designed to operate in conjunction with other parts of the system.

utility program A SERVICE ROUTINE.

utility routine A SERVICE ROUTINE.

V

VAB *abbr.* VOICE ANSWER BACK.

validity check A check designed to ensure that a code group is in fact an element of the code in use.

value *n.* **1** The number or quantity represented by a variable or function under a specified set of conditions. **2** CODE VALUE.

variable *n.* A symbol that can represent any

one of a given set of numbers or quantities, it being understood that the indicated result of an operation is not a variable although it may contain variables. Consider the product *ab*; it may vary through a set of values. If this is the case, then *a* is a variable, or *b* is a variable, or both are variables, but *ab* itself is not considered a variable.

variable connector In flowcharting, a connector that represents a branchpoint or an interconnection in which the number of points exceeds two.

variable-length record Indicating a file in which no constraints are placed on the lengths of the constituent records.

variable-point Indicating a system of numeration in which the RADIX POINT is explicitly indicated by a special character.

variolosser *n.* A variable ATTENUATOR whose loss is determined by a control signal.

vector *n.* A mathematical quantity, as displacement, velocity, acceleration, etc., that is uniquely specified by its magnitude and direction. A more careful definition of a vector requires that it be invariant under a translation or rotation of the coordinate system in which it is described.

Venn diagram A diagram in which sets are represented as areas whose boundaries are closed curves or figures. (See illustration in opposite column.)

verifier *n.* A device similar to a card punch that checks the data inscribed on a card by means of a rekeying process, indicating when the data keyed and the data already punched do not agree.

verify *v.* **1** To establish that (transcription or some other operation on data) has been ac-curately performed. **2** To establish that (the punching of data onto cards) has been correctly done.

vertical tabulation character A control character that causes the printing or display position to be moved a specified number of lines at right angles to the line of printing.

vestigial sideband transmission A form of carrier transmission in which the carrier and one sideband are transmitted normally, the remaining sideband being strongly attenuated but not completely suppressed.

VENN Diagram

$A + B$
$(A \cup B)$

$A \cdot B'$
$(A \cap B')$

$A \cdot B$
$(A \cap B)$

$B \cdot A'$
$(B \cap A')$

$A' \cdot B'$
$A' \cap B'$

Set A   Set B

V format A data set format in which logical records vary in length and include a length indicator, and in which records of this type can be combined into blocks which vary in length, each block having its own length indicator.

virtual *adj.* Apparent; not actual or absolute, as the addresses in a relocatable routine.

visual scanner An OPTICAL SCANNER.

VOGAD *abbr.* VOICE-OPERATED GAIN-ADJUSTING DEVICE.

voice answer back An arrangement in which a computer can provide voice responses to inquiries made from telephone-type terminals, the response being selected from a vocabulary of prerecorded or coded voice signals.

voice-frequency carrier telegraphy Carrier telegraphy in which the frequency spectrum of the modulated carrier as transmitted lies within the capabilities of a voice-grade channel.

voice-grade channel A channel whose bandwidth is sufficient for the adequate transmission of speech signals, the usual bandwidth for such a channel extending from 300–3000 hz. It is entirely possible (and frequent) for signals other than speech to be transmitted via such channels provided that the bandwidth limitations are not exceeded.

voice-operated device In telephony, any of various devices whose operations are initiated by the presence of a signal or by some characteristic of the signal when it is present, used in the performance of various line control operations, as echo suppression.

Voice-Operated Gain-Adjusting Device In telephony, a device that is in essence a COMPRESSOR, used to reduce the fluctuations in level that are common in speech and thus improve the average signal-to-noise ratio. It requires no complementary device at the receiving end, and while it enhances intelligibility it does so at the expense of some of the natural quality of the transmitted speech.

voice unit A measure of the average amplitude of an electrical signal that represents speech or other similar program material; a VOLUME UNIT.

void *n.* In character recognition, the absence of ink within the outline of a character that was intended to be printed.

volatile dynamic storage A DYNAMIC STORAGE device in which the maintenance of the stored information depends on the maintenance of an external supply of power.

volatile storage A type of storage in which the maintenance of the stored data depends on the maintenance of an external supply of power.

volume *n.* **1** That portion of a single unit of storage media which is accessible to a single read/write mechanism. **2** The magnitude of a complex electrical signal such as one that represents speech or some similar audio signal.

volume indicator A VU METER.

volume table of contents A table associated with and describing every data set in a direct access volume.

volume test A program checkout procedure in which a volume of data is actually processed and malfunctions noted.

volume unit A decibel defined with respect to a reference power level of one milliwatt rms delivered into a 600–ohm resistive load at a signal frequency of 1000 hz.

V response An answer made to a response of a teletypewriter terminal to a poll or address selection.

VT *abbr.* The VERTICAL TABULATION CHARACTER.

VTOC *abbr.* VOLUME TABLE OF CONTENTS.

VU *abbr.* **1** VOICE UNIT. **2** VOLUME UNIT.

VU indicator *abbr.* Volume unit indicator.

VU meter An electric indicating meter having specified internal damping of its movement, used to indicate VOLUME UNITS (VOICE UNITS).

W

wait condition Of a task, a condition such that transition into the ready state depends on the occurrence of one or more events.

WATS *abbr.* WIDE AREA TELEPHONE SERVICE.

waveform *n.* A graphical representation in which the amplitude of a wave is plotted against time.

way station In Western Union terminology, any station on a multipoint circuit.

weight 1 *n.* SIGNIFICANCE. **2** *n.* In a set of terms of the form $a_n x_n$, each of the multipliers a_i associated with each x_i. **3** *v.* To apply varying multipliers to (each of a set of variables or each of a set of values of the same variable).

Who are you? The ENQUIRY CHARACTER.

Wide Area Telephone Service A form of telephone service in which the customer is enabled to dial calls within a specified area for a flat monthly charge, the amount of the charge depending only on the size of the area and not on the number or length of calls.

width *n.* STROKE WIDTH.

willful intercept The interception of messages addressed to stations at which there is equipment or line malfunction.

wiring board A PLUGBOARD.

wired-program computer A computer in which the operations performed or their sequence is controlled by the placement and interconnection of wires, as on a plugboard.

word *n.* A succession of characters or bits that is defined as a single entity according to some criterion as length, content, or the like.

word length The number of bits or characters contained in a WORD.

word-mark A control character that indicates the beginning or end of a WORD.

word time In a serial access storage device, the time that elapses between the instants at which corresponding parts of successive words appear.

working storage TEMPORARY STORAGE.

worst case The case in which the maximum stress is placed on a system, as in making it error-prone, or inefficient.

wpm, WPM *abbr.* Words per minute.

wrap-around storage An arrangement of core storage in which the lowest numbered storage location is the effective successor of the highest numbered one.

write *v.* To enter (data) into some form of storage.

WRU In USASCII, the ENQUIRY CHARACTER; WHO ARE YOU?

XYZ

X-Off Transmitter off.

X-On Transmitter on.

X-punch On a Hollerith card, a punch in the second row from the top.

xy recorder A device that traces the relation between a pair of variables onto a set of plane RECTANGULAR COORDINATES.

Y-punch On a Hollerith card, a punch in the uppermost row, used often for control information or to indicate the sign of a number punched in the same column.

zero *n.* In a system of numbers, the identity element with respect to addition, that is, a number (0) such that $a + 0 = 0 + a = a$, and $a \times 0 = 0 \times a = a$, where a is an arbitrarily chosen number.

zero-access storage Loosely, a storage in which the access time is always short enough to be considered negligible.

zero-level address An IMMEDIATE ADDRESS.

zero-punch On a Hollerith card, a punch in the third row from the top.

zero suppression The removal from the representation of a number zeros that are nonsignificant, that is, zeros that occupy the high-order positions of a numeral when preceded by no other digit.

zero transmission level reference point In a communications circuit, a point at which the signal level is arbitrarily defined as 0 *db*, all other signal levels being referred to the level at this point.

zone punch On a Hollerith card, an X-PUNCH, a Y-PUNCH, or a ZERO-PUNCH.

APPENDIXES

MATHEMATICAL SYMBOLS

$+$	Plus; positive; sign of addition; or	Σ	Summation of
$-$	Minus; negative; sign of subtraction	$\overset{n}{\underset{1}{\Sigma}}$	Summation of n terms, one for each positive integer from 1 to n
$\pm$	Plus or minus	Π	Product of
$\mp$	Minus or plus	$\overset{n}{\underset{1}{\Pi}}$	Product of n terms, one for each positive integer from 1 to n
$\times, \cdot$	Multiplied by		
$\div, :$	Divided by	$\int$	Integral of
$=, ::$	Equals; equivalence	$\int_b^a$	Definite integral between limits a and b
$\cong$	Approximately equal; congruent	$\doteqdot, \rightarrow$	Approaches as a limit
$>$	Greater than	$f(x), F(x), \phi(x)$	Function of x
$<$	Less than	Δ	Increment of, as Δy
$/$	Is not; does not: drawn through another symbol, as $a \neq b$, a is not equal to b	d	Differential, as dx
$\geqq$	Greater than or equal to	$\dfrac{dy}{dx}, f'(x)$	Derivative of $y = f(x)$ with respect to x
$\leqq$	Less than or equal to		
$\sim$	Similar to; equivalent	δ	Variation as δy
$\therefore$	Therefore	π	Pi; the ratio of the circumference and a diameter of the same circle; 3.14159...
$\because$	Since; because		
$\equiv$	Identical; identically equal to	$n!, \underline{n}$	n factorial; factorial n
$\propto$	Directly proportional to; varies directly as	$(), [], \{\}$	Indicate that the enclosed symbols are to be treated as a single number
∞	Infinity	$-$	Indicates that the symbols below it are to be treated as a single number, as $\overline{PQ}^2$
i	Square root of minus one		
$a_1, a_2,$ etc.	Particular values of a (a variable)	$\angle$	Angle
a^n	a raised to the n power	$\parallel$	Parallel to
$\frac{a}{b}$	a divided by b	$\perp$	Perpendicular to; perpendicular
$\sqrt{a}$	Square root of a. See RADICAL SIGN.	$\triangle$	Triangle
$\sqrt[n]{a}$	nth root of a	$\llcorner$	Right angle
e, ϵ	Base of natural system of logarithms; 2.718...	$'$	Minutes of arc; prime; not
		$''$	Seconds of arc; double prime
$\cdot$	And	$\rightarrow$	Implication
$\oplus$	Exclusive or	$A, B,$ etc.	Particular sets
$\cup$	Union of two sets	A'	Complement of A; not A
$\cap$	Intersection of two sets	∂	Partial derivative sign

E.I.A. STANDARD CODING FOR
1 INCH WIDE, EIGHT TRACK TAPE

TAPE PUNCH	8 / EL	7 / X	6 / O	5 / CH	4 / 8	•	3 / 4	2 / 2	1 / 1
0			●			•			
1						•			●
2						•		●	
3				●		•		●	●
4						•	●		
5				●		•	●		●
6				●		•	●	●	
7						•	●	●	●
8					●	•			
9				●	●	•			●
a		●	●			•			●
b		●	●			•		●	
c		●	●	●		•		●	●
d		●	●			•	●		
e		●	●	●		•	●		●
f		●	●	●		•	●	●	
g		●	●			•	●	●	●
h		●	●		●	•			
i		●	●	●	●	•			●
j		●		●		•			●
k		●		●		•		●	
l		●				•		●	●
m		●		●		•	●		
n		●				•	●		●
o		●				•	●	●	
p		●		●		•	●	●	●
q		●		●	●	•			
r		●			●	•			●
s			●	●		•		●	
t			●			•		●	●
u			●	●		•	●		
v			●			•	●		●
w			●			•	●	●	
x			●	●		•	●	●	●
y			●	●	●	•			
z			●		●	•			●
(PERIOD) .		●	●		●	•	●	●	
(COMMA) ,		●	●		●	•	●		
/		●	●		●	•			●
(PLUS) +		●			●	•	●		
(MINUS) −		●				•			
SPACE					●	•			
DELETE	●	●	●	●	●	•	●	●	●
CARR. RET. OR END OF BLOCK	●					•			
BACK SPACE			●		●	•		●	
TAB			●	●	●	•	●		●
END OF RECORD					●	•	●	●	
LEADER						•			
BLANK TYPE						•			
UPPER CASE	●	●	●	●		•	●		
LOWER CASE	●	●	●	●		•			●

PAGE AND TAPE TELETYPEWRITER CODES

CHARACTERS				CODE WORDS				
PAGE		TAPE						
UC	LC	UC	LC					
		·	A	1	1	0	0	0
		?	B	1	0	0	1	1
		:	C	0	1	1	1	0
		$	D	1	0	0	1	0
		3	E	1	0	0	0	0
			F	1	0	1	1	0
		&	G	0	1	0	1	1
#		£	H	0	0	1	0	1
		8	I	0	1	1	0	0
		BELL	J	1	1	0	1	0
		(	K	1	1	1	1	0
		)	L	0	1	0	0	1
.		%	M	0	0	1	1	1
,		'	N	0	0	1	1	0
		9	O	0	0	0	1	1
		0	P	0	1	1	0	1
		1	Q	1	1	1	0	1
		4	R	0	1	0	1	0
'		¶	S	1	0	1	0	0
		5	T	0	0	0	0	1
		7	U	1	1	1	0	0
		;	V	0	1	1	1	1
		2	W	1	1	0	0	1
		/	X	1	0	1	1	1
		6	Y	1	0	1	0	1
		''	Z	1	0	0	0	1
		SPACE		0	0	1	0	0
CAR. RET		,	.	0	0	0	1	0
LINE FEED		#	=	0	1	0	0	0
		FIGURES		1	1	0	1	1
		LETTERS		1	1	1	1	1
		BLANK		0	0	0	0	0

PROGRAM FLOWCHART SYMBOLS

SYMBOL	REPRESENTS
	PROCESSING A group of program instructions which perform a processing function of the program.
	INPUT/OUTPUT Any function of an input/output device (making information available for processing, recording processing information, tape positioning, etc.).
	DECISION The decision function used to document points in the program where a branch to alternate paths is possible based upon variable conditions.
	PROGRAM MODIFICATION An instruction or group of instructions which changes the program.
	PREDEFINED PROCESS A group of operations not detailed in the particular set of flowcharts.
	TERMINAL The beginning, end, or a point of interruption in a program.
	CONNECTOR An entry from, or an exit to, another part of the program flowchart.
	OFFPAGE CONNECTOR A connector used instead of the connector symbol to designate entry to or exit from a page.
◁ ▷ ▽ △	**FLOW DIRECTION** The direction of processing or data flow.
	ANNOTATION The addition of descriptive comments or explanatory notes as clarification.

LOGIC SYMBOLS

AND gate   **OR gate**   **NAND gate**

NOR gate   Invert   Flip-Flops Clocks, Non-Gate Functions

SYSTEM FLOWCHART SYMBOLS

PROCESSING
A major processing function.

INPUT/ OUTPUT
Any type of medium or data.

PUNCHED CARD
All varieties of punched cards including stubs.

PERFORATED TAPE
Paper or plastic, chad or chadless.

DOCUMENT
Paper documents and reports of all varieties.

TRANSMITTAL TAPE
A proof or adding machine tape or similar batch-control information.

MAGNETIC TAPE

DISK, DRUM, RANDOM ACCESS

OFFLINE STORAGE
Offline storage of either paper, cards, magnetic or perforated tape.

DISPLAY
Information displayed by plotters or video devices.

ONLINE KEYBOARD
Information supplied to or by a computer utilizing an online device.

SORTING, COLLATING
An operation on sorting or collating equipment.

CLERICAL OPERATION
A manual offline operation not requiring mechanical aid.

AUXILIARY OPERATION
A machine operation supplementing the main processing function.

KEYING OPERATION
An operation utilizing a key-driven device.

COMMUNICATION LINK
The automatic transmission of information from one location to another via communication lines.

FLOW ◁ ▷ ▽ △   The direction of processing or data flow.

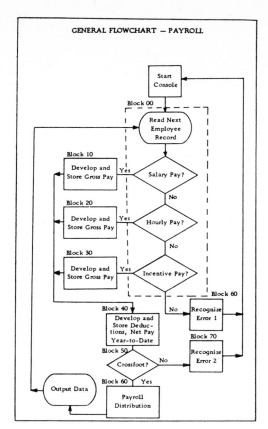

GENERAL FLOWCHART — PAYROLL

Start Console

Block 00

Read Next Employee Record

Block 10 — Develop and Store Gross Pay — Yes — Salary Pay?

No

Block 20 — Develop and Store Gross Pay — Yes — Hourly Pay?

No

Block 30 — Develop and Store Gross Pay — Yes — Incentive Pay?

Block 40 — Develop and Store Deductions, Net Pay Year-to-Date — No — Block 60 Recognize Error 1

Block 50 — Crossfoot? — No — Block 70 Recognize Error 2

Block 60 — Yes — Payroll Distribution

Output Data

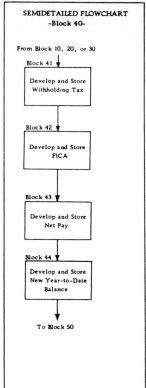

SEMIDETAILED FLOWCHART
-Block 40-

From Block 10, 20, or 30

Block 41 — Develop and Store Withholding Tax

Block 42 — Develop and Store FICA

Block 43 — Develop and Store Net Pay

Block 44 — Develop and Store New Year-to-Date Balance

To Block 50

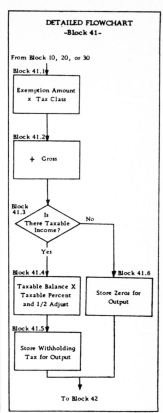

DETAILED FLOWCHART
-Block 41-

From Block 10, 20, or 30

Block 41.1 — Exemption Amount x Tax Class

Block 41.2 — + Gross

Block 41.3 — Is There Taxable Income? — No

Yes

Block 41.4 — Taxable Balance X Taxable Percent and 1/2 Adjust

Block 41.6 — Store Zeros for Output

Block 41.5 — Store Withholding Tax for Output

To Block 42

---

*A system for producing and revising flowcharts by using a data processing system and a flowcharting language is described in "IBM System/360 FLOWCHART", an application description and

programmer's manual (H20-0199).

**A particularly useful manual in connection with block diagramming is Flowcharting Techniques, (C20-8152).

CHARACTER CODES

EBCDIC CODE	CARD PUNCH COMBINATION	PRINTER GRAPHIC	DECIMAL	HEXADECIMAL
00000000	12,0,9,8,1		0	00
00000001	12,9,1		1	01
00000010	12,9,2		2	02
00000011	12,9,3		3	03
00000100	12,9,4		4	04
00000101	12,9,5		5	05
00000110	12,9,6		6	06
00000111	12,9,7		7	07
00001000	12,9,8		8	08
00001001	12,9,8,1		9	09
00001010	12,9,8,2		10	0A
00001011	12,9,8,3		11	0B
00001100	12,9,8,4		12	0C
00001101	12,9,8,5		13	0D
00001110	12,9,8,6		14	0E
00001111	12,9,8,7		15	0F
00010000	12,11,9,8,1		16	10
00010001	11,9,1		17	11
00010010	11,9,2		18	12
00010011	11,9,3		19	13
00010100	11,9,4		20	14
00010101	11,9,5		21	15
00010110	11,9,6		22	16
00010111	11,9,7		23	17
00011000	11,9,8		24	18
00011001	11,9,8,1		25	19
00011010	11,9,8,2		26	1A
00011011	11,9,8,3		27	1B
00011100	11,9,8,4		28	1C
00011101	11,9,8,5		29	1D
00011110	11,9,8,6		30	1E
00011111	11,9,8,7		31	1F
00100000	11,0,9,8,1		32	20
00100001	0,9,1		33	21
00100010	0,9,2		34	22
00100011	0,9,3		35	23
00100100	0,9,4		36	24
00100101	0,9,5		37	25
00100110	0,9,6		38	26
00100111	0,9,7		39	27
00101000	0,9,8		40	28
00101001	0,9,8,1		41	29
00101010	0,9,8,2		42	2A
00101011	0,9,8,3		43	2B
00101100	0,9,8,4		44	2C
00101101	0,9,8,5		45	2D

CHARACTER CODES

EBCDIC CODE	CARD PUNCH COMBINATION	PRINTER GRAPHIC	DECIMAL	HEXADECIMAL
00101110	0,9,8,6		46	2E
00101111	0,9,8,7		47	2F
00110000	12,11,0,9,8,1		48	30
00110001	9,1		49	31
00110010	9,2		50	32
00110011	9,3		51	33
00110100	9,4		52	34
00110101	9,5		53	35
00110110	9,6		54	36
00110111	9,7		55	37
00111000	9,8		56	38
00111001	9,8,1		57	39
00111010	9,8,2		58	3A
00111011	9,8,3		59	3B
00111100	9,8,4		60	3C
00111101	9,8,5		61	3D
00111110	9,8,6		62	3E
00111111	9,8,7		63	3F
01000000		blank	64	40
01000001	12,0,9,1		65	41
01000010	12,0,9,2		66	42
01000011	12,0,9,3		67	43
01000100	12,0,9,4		68	44
01000101	12,0,9,5		69	45
01000110	12,0,9,6		70	46
01000111	12,0,9,7		71	47
01001000	12,0,9,8		72	48
01001001	12,8,1		73	49
01001010	12,8,2		74	4A
01001011	12,8,3	.(period)	75	4B
01001100	12,8,4	<-	76	4C
01001101	12,8,5	(	77	4D
01001110	12,8,6	+	78	4E
01001111	12,8,7		79	4F
01010000	12	&	80	50
01010001	12,11,9,1		81	51
01010010	12,11,9,2		82	52
01010011	12,11,9,3		83	53
01010100	12,11,9,4		84	54
01010101	12,11,9,5		85	55
01010110	12,11,9,6		86	56
01010111	12,11,9,7		87	57
01011000	12,11,9,8		88	58
01011001	11,8,1		89	59
01011010	11,8,2		90	5A
01011011	11,8,3	$	91	5B

CHARACTER CODES

EBCDIC CODE	CARD PUNCH COMBINATION	PRINTER GRAPHIC	DECIMAL	HEXADECIMAL
01011100	11,8,4	*	92	5C
01011101	11,8,5	)	93	5D
01011110	11,8,6		94	5E
01011111	11,8,7		95	5F
01100000	11	–	96	60
01100001	0,1	/	97	61
01100010	11,0,9,2		98	62
01100011	11,0,9,3		99	63
01100100	11,0,9,4		100	64
01100101	11,0,9,5		101	65
01100110	11,0,9,6		102	66
01100111	11,0,9,7		103	67
01101000	11,0,9,8		104	68
01101001	0,8,1		105	69
01101010	12,11		106	6A
01101011	0,8,3	,	107	6B
01101100	0,8,4	%	108	6C
01101101	0,8,5		109	6D
01101110	0,8,6		110	6E
01101111	0,8,7		111	6F
01110000	12,11,0		112	70
01110001	12,11,0,9,1		113	71
01110010	12,11,0,9,2		114	72
01110011	12,11,0,9,3		115	73
01110100	12,11,0,9,4		116	74
01110101	12,11,0,9,5		117	75
01110110	12,11,0,9,6		118	76
01110111	12,11,0,9,7		119	77
01111000	12,11,0,9,8		120	78
01111001	8,1		121	79
01111010	8,2		122	7A
01111011	8,3	#	123	7B
01111100	8,4	@	124	7C
01111101	8,5	'	125	7D
01111110	8,6	=	126	7E
01111111	8,7		127	7F
10000000	12,0,8,1		128	80
10000001	12,0,1		129	81
10000010	12,0,2		130	82
10000011	12,0,3		131	83
10000100	12,0,4		132	84
10000101	12,0,5		133	85
10000110	12,0,6		134	86
10000111	12,0,7		135	87
10001000	12,0,8		136	88
10001001	12,0,9		137	89

CHARACTER CODES

EBCDIC CODE	CARD PUNCH COMBINATION	PRINTER GRAPHIC	DECIMAL	HEXADECIMAL
10001010	12,0,8,2		138	8A
10001011	12,0,8,3		139	8B
10001100	12,0,8,4		140	8C
10001101	12,0,8,5		141	8D
10001110	12,0,8,6		142	8E
10001111	12,0,8,7		143	8F
10010000	12,11,8,1		144	90
10010001	12,11,1		145	91
10010010	12,11,2		146	92
10010011	12,11,3		147	93
10010100	12,11,4		148	94
10010101	12,11,5		149	95
10010110	12,11,6		150	96
10010111	12,11,7		151	97
10011000	12,11,8		152	98
10011001	12,11,9		153	99
10011010	12,11,8,2		154	9A
10011011	12,11,8,3		155	9B
10011100	12,11,8,4		156	9C
10011101	12,11,8,5		157	9D
10011110	12,11,8,6		158	9E
10011111	12,11,8,7		159	9F
10100000	11,0,8,1		160	A0
10100001	11,0,1		161	A1
10100010	11,0,2		162	A2
10100011	11,0,3		163	A3
10100100	11,0,4		164	A4
10100101	11,0,5		165	A5
10100110	11,0,6		166	A6
10100111	11,0,7		167	A7
10101000	11,0,8		168	A8
10101001	11,0,9		169	A9
10101010	11,0,8,2		170	AA
10101011	11,0,8,3		171	AB
10101100	11,0,8,4		172	AC
10101101	11,0,8,5		173	AD
10101110	11,0,8,6		174	AE
10101111	11,0,8,7		175	AF
10110000	12,11,0,8,1		176	B0
10110001	12,11,0,1		177	B1
10110010	12,11,0,2		178	B2
10110011	12,11,0,3		179	B3
10110100	12,11,0,4		180	B4
10110101	12,11,0,5		181	B5
10110110	12,11,0,6		182	B6
10110111	12,11,0,7		183	B7

CHARACTER CODES

EBCDIC CODE	CARD PUNCH COMBINATION	PRINTER GRAPHIC	DECIMAL	HEXADECIMAL
10111000	12,11,0,8		184	B8
10111001	12,11,0,9		185	B9
10111010	12,11,0,8,2		186	BA
10111011	12,11,0,8,3		187	BB
10111100	12,11,0,8,4		188	BC
10111101	12,11,0,8,5		189	BD
10111110	12,11,0,8,6		190	BE
10111111	12,11,0,8,7		191	BF
11000000	12,0		192	C0
11000001	12,1	A	193	C1
11000010	12,2	B	194	C2
11000011	12,3	C	195	C3
11000100	12,4	D	196	C4
11000101	12,5	E	197	C5
11000110	12,6	F	198	C6
11000111	12,7	G	199	C7
11001000	12,8	H	200	C8
11001001	12,9	I	201	C9
11001010	12,0,9,8,2		202	CA
11001011	12,0,9,8,3		203	CB
11001100	12,0,9,8,4		204	CC
11001101	12,0,9,8,5		205	CD
11001110	12,0,9,8,6		206	CE
11001111	12,0,9,8,7		207	CF
11010000	11,0		208	D0
11010001	11,1	J	209	D1
11010010	11,2	K	210	D2
11010011	11,3	L	211	D3
11010100	11,4	M	212	D4
11010101	11,5	N	213	D5
11010110	11,6	O	214	D6
11010111	11,7	P	215	D7
11011000	11,8	Q	216	D8
11011001	11,9	R	217	D9
11011010	12,11,9,8,2		218	DA
11011011	12,11,9,8,3		219	DB
11011100	12,11,9,8,4		220	DC
11011101	12,11,9,8,5		221	DD
11011110	12,11,9,8,6		222	DE
11011111	12,11,9,8,7		223	DF
11100000	0,8,2		224	E0
11100001	11,0,9,1		225	E1
11100010	0,2	S	226	E2
11100011	0,3	T	227	E3
11100100	0,4	U	228	E4
11100101	0,5	V	229	E5

CHARACTER CODES

EBCDIC CODE	CARD PUNCH COMBINATION	PRINTER GRAPHIC	DECIMAL	HEXADECIMAL
11100110	0,6	W	230	E6
11100111	0,7	X	231	E7
11101000	0,8	Y	232	E8
11101001	0,9	Z	233	E9
11101010	11,0,9,8,2		234	EA
11101011	11,0,9,8,3		235	EB
11101100	11,0,9,8,4		236	EC
11101101	11,0,9,8,5		237	ED
11101110	11,0,9,8,6		238	EE
11101111	11,0,9,8,7		239	EF
11110000	0	0	240	F0
11110001	1	1	241	F1
11110010	2	2	242	F2
11110011	3	3	243	F3
11110100	4	4	244	F4
11110101	5	5	245	F5
11110110	6	6	246	F6
11110111	7	7	247	F7
11111000	8	8	248	F8
11111001	9	9	249	F9
11111010	12,11,0,9,8,2		250	FA
11111011	12,11,0,9,8,3		251	FB
11111100	12,11,0,9,8,4		252	FC
11111101	12,11,0,9,8,5		253	FD
11111110	12,11,0,9,8,6		254	FE
11111111	12,11,0,9,8,7		255	FF

The table in this appendix provides for direct conversion of decimal and hexadecimal numbers in these ranges:

Hexadecimal	Decimal
000 to FFF	0000 to 4095

Decimal numbers (0000-4095) are given within the 8-part table. The first two characters (high-order) of hexadecimal numbers (000-FFF) are given in the left-hand column of the table, and the third character is arranged across the top of each part of the table. Thus, to find the decimal equivalent of the hex number 0C9, look for 0C in the left column, and across under the column labeled 9. The decimal number is 0201.

To convert from decimal to hexadecimal, look up the decimal number within the table and read the hexadecimal number by a combination of the hex characters to the left and above the decimal number. For example, decimal number 123 has the hex equivalent of 07B, and decimal 1478 has the hex equivalent of 5C6.

For numbers outside the range of the table, add the following values to the table figures:

Hexadecimal	Decimal
1000	4096
2000	8192
3000	12288
4000	16384
5000	20480
6000	24576
7000	28672
8000	32768
9000	36864
A000	40960
B000	45056
C000	49152
D000	53248
E000	57344
F000	61440

HEXADECIMAL–DECIMAL NUMBER CONVERSION TABLE

	0	1	2	3	4	5	6	7	8	9	A	B	C	D	E	F
00	0000	0001	0002	0003	0004	0005	0006	0007	0008	0009	0010	0011	0012	0013	0014	0015
01	0016	0017	0018	0019	0020	0021	0022	0023	0024	0025	0026	0027	0028	0029	0030	0031
02	0032	0033	0034	0035	0036	0037	0038	0039	0040	0041	0042	0043	0044	0045	0046	0047
03	0048	0049	0050	0051	0052	0053	0054	0055	0056	0057	0058	0059	0060	0061	0062	0063
04	0064	0065	0066	0067	0068	0069	0070	0071	0072	0073	0074	0075	0076	0077	0078	0079
05	0080	0081	0082	0083	0084	0085	0086	0087	0088	0089	0090	0091	0092	0093	0094	0095
06	0096	0097	0098	0099	0100	0101	0102	0103	0104	0105	0106	0107	0108	0109	0110	0111
07	0112	0113	0114	0115	0116	0117	0118	0119	0120	0121	0122	0123	0124	0125	0126	0127
08	0128	0129	0130	0131	0132	0133	0134	0135	0136	0137	0138	0139	0140	0141	0142	0143
09	0144	0145	0146	0147	0148	0149	0150	0151	0152	0153	0154	0155	0156	0157	0158	0159
0A	0160	0161	0162	0163	0164	0165	0166	0167	0168	0169	0170	0171	0172	0173	0174	0175
0B	0176	0177	0178	0179	0180	0181	0182	0183	0184	0185	0186	0187	0188	0189	0190	0191
0C	0192	0193	0194	0195	0196	0197	0198	0199	0200	0201	0202	0203	0204	0205	0206	0207
0D	0208	0209	0210	0211	0212	0213	0214	0215	0216	0217	0218	0219	0220	0221	0222	0223
0E	0224	0225	0226	0227	0228	0229	0230	0231	0232	0233	0234	0235	0236	0237	0238	0239
0F	0240	0241	0242	0243	0244	0245	0246	0247	0248	0249	0250	0251	0252	0253	0254	0255
10	0256	0257	0258	0259	0260	0261	0262	0263	0264	0265	0266	0267	0268	0269	0270	0271
11	0272	0273	0274	0275	0276	0277	0278	0279	0280	0281	0282	0283	0284	0285	0286	0287
12	0288	0289	0290	0291	0292	0293	0294	0295	0296	0297	0298	0299	0300	0301	0302	0303
13	0304	0305	0306	0307	0308	0309	0310	0311	0312	0313	0314	0315	0316	0317	0318	0319
14	0320	0321	0322	0323	0324	0325	0326	0327	0328	0329	0330	0331	0332	0333	0334	0335
15	0336	0337	0338	0339	0340	0341	0342	0343	0344	0345	0346	0347	0348	0349	0350	0351
16	0352	0353	0354	0355	0356	0357	0358	0359	0360	0361	0362	0363	0364	0365	0366	0367
17	0368	0369	0370	0371	0372	0373	0374	0375	0376	0377	0378	0379	0380	0381	0382	0383
18	0384	0385	0386	0387	0388	0389	0390	0391	0392	0393	0394	0395	0396	0397	0398	0399
19	0400	0401	0402	0403	0404	0405	0406	0407	0408	0409	0410	0411	0412	0413	0414	0415
1A	0416	0417	0418	0419	0420	0421	0422	0423	0424	0425	0426	0427	0428	0429	0430	0431
1B	0432	0433	0434	0435	0436	0437	0438	0439	0440	0441	0442	0443	0444	0445	0446	0447
1C	0448	0449	0450	0451	0452	0453	0454	0455	0456	0457	0458	0459	0460	0461	0462	0463
1D	0464	0465	0466	0467	0468	0469	0470	0471	0472	0473	0474	0475	0476	0477	0478	0479
1E	0480	0481	0482	0483	0484	0485	0486	0487	0488	0489	0490	0491	0492	0493	0494	0495
1F	0496	0497	0498	0499	0500	0501	0502	0503	0504	0505	0506	0507	0508	0509	0510	0511

HEXADECIMAL-DECIMAL NUMBER CONVERSION TABLE

	0	1	2	3	4	5	6	7	8	9	A	B	C	D	E	F
20	0512	0513	0514	0515	0516	0517	0518	0519	0520	0521	0522	0523	0524	0525	0526	0527
21	0528	0529	0530	0531	0532	0533	0534	0535	0536	0537	0538	0539	0540	0541	0542	0543
22	0544	0545	0546	0547	0548	0549	0550	0551	0552	0553	0554	0555	0556	0557	0558	0559
23	0560	0561	0562	0563	0564	0565	0566	0567	0568	0569	0570	0571	0572	0573	0574	0575
24	0576	0577	0578	0579	0580	0581	0582	0583	0584	0585	0586	0587	0588	0589	0590	0591
25	0592	0593	0594	0595	0596	0597	0598	0599	0600	0601	0602	0603	0604	0605	0606	0607
26	0608	0609	0610	0611	0612	0613	0614	0615	0616	0617	0618	0619	0620	0621	0622	0623
27	0624	0625	0626	0627	0628	0629	0630	0631	0632	0633	0634	0635	0636	0637	0638	0639
28	0640	0641	0642	0643	0644	0645	0646	0647	0648	0649	0650	0651	0652	0653	0654	0655
29	0656	0657	0658	0659	0660	0661	0662	0663	0664	0665	0666	0667	0668	0669	0670	0671
2A	0672	0673	0674	0675	0676	0677	0678	0679	0680	0681	0682	0683	0684	0685	0686	0687
2B	0688	0689	0690	0691	0692	0693	0694	0695	0696	0697	0698	0699	0700	0701	0702	0703
2C	0704	0705	0706	0707	0708	0709	0710	0711	0712	0713	0714	0715	0716	0717	0718	0719
2D	0720	0721	0722	0723	0724	0725	0726	0727	0728	0729	0730	0731	0732	0733	0734	0735
2E	0736	0737	0738	0739	0740	0741	0742	0743	0744	0745	0746	0747	0748	0749	0750	0751
2F	0752	0753	0754	0755	0756	0757	0758	0759	0760	0761	0762	0763	0764	0765	0766	0767
30	0768	0769	0770	0771	0772	0773	0774	0775	0776	0777	0778	0779	0780	0781	0782	0783
31	0784	0785	0786	0787	0788	0789	0790	0791	0792	0793	0794	0795	0796	0797	0798	0799
32	0800	0801	0802	0803	0804	0805	0806	0807	0808	0809	0810	0811	0812	0813	0814	0815
33	0816	0817	0818	0819	0820	0821	0822	0823	0824	0825	0826	0827	0828	0829	0830	0831
34	0832	0833	0834	0835	0836	0837	0838	0839	0840	0841	0842	0843	0844	0845	0846	0847
35	0848	0849	0850	0851	0852	0853	0854	0855	0856	0857	0858	0859	0860	0861	0862	0863
36	0864	0865	0866	0867	0868	0869	0870	0871	0872	0873	0874	0875	0876	0877	0878	0879
37	0880	0881	0882	0883	0884	0885	0886	0887	0888	0889	0890	0891	0892	0893	0894	0895
38	0896	0897	0898	0899	0900	0901	0902	0903	0904	0905	0906	0907	0908	0909	0910	0911
39	0912	0913	0914	0915	0916	0917	0918	0919	0920	0921	0922	0923	0924	0925	0926	0927
3A	0928	0929	0930	0931	0932	0933	0934	0935	0936	0937	0938	0939	0940	0941	0942	0943
3B	0944	0945	0946	0947	0948	0949	0950	0951	0952	0953	0954	0955	0956	0957	0958	0959
3C	0960	0961	0962	0963	0964	0965	0966	0967	0968	0969	0970	0971	0972	0973	0974	0975
3D	0976	0977	0978	0979	0980	0981	0982	0983	0984	0985	0986	0987	0988	0989	0990	0991
3E	0992	0993	0994	0995	0996	0997	0998	0999	1000	1001	1002	1003	1004	1005	1006	1007
3F	1008	1009	1010	1011	1012	1013	1014	1015	1016	1017	1018	1019	1020	1021	1022	1023

HEXADECIMAL-DECIMAL NUMBER CONVERSION TABLE

	0	1	2	3	4	5	6	7	8	9	A	B	C	D	E	F
40	1024	1025	1026	1027	1028	1029	1030	1031	1032	1033	1034	1035	1036	1037	1038	1039
41	1040	1041	1042	1043	1044	1045	1046	1047	1048	1049	1050	1051	1052	1053	1054	1055
42	1056	1057	1058	1059	1060	1061	1062	1063	1064	1065	1066	1067	1068	1069	1070	1071
43	1072	1073	1074	1075	1076	1077	1078	1079	1080	1081	1082	1083	1084	1085	1086	1087
44	1088	1089	1090	1091	1092	1093	1094	1095	1096	1097	1098	1099	1100	1101	1102	1103
45	1104	1105	1106	1107	1108	1109	1110	1111	1112	1113	1114	1115	1116	1117	1118	1119
46	1120	1121	1122	1123	1124	1125	1126	1127	1128	1129	1130	1131	1132	1133	1134	1135
47	1136	1137	1138	1139	1140	1141	1142	1143	1144	1145	1146	1147	1148	1149	1150	1151
48	1152	1153	1154	1155	1156	1157	1158	1159	1160	1161	1162	1163	1164	1165	1166	1167
49	1168	1169	1170	1171	1172	1173	1174	1175	1176	1177	1178	1179	1180	1181	1182	1183
4A	1184	1185	1186	1187	1188	1189	1190	1191	1192	1193	1194	1195	1196	1197	1198	1199
4B	1200	1201	1202	1203	1204	1205	1206	1207	1208	1209	1210	1211	1212	1213	1214	1215
4C	1216	1217	1218	1219	1220	1221	1222	1223	1224	1225	1226	1227	1228	1229	1230	1231
4D	1232	1233	1234	1235	1236	1237	1238	1239	1240	1241	1242	1243	1244	1245	1246	1247
4E	1248	1249	1250	1251	1252	1253	1254	1255	1256	1257	1258	1259	1260	1261	1262	1263
4F	1264	1265	1266	1267	1268	1269	1270	1271	1272	1273	1274	1275	1276	1277	1278	1279
50	1280	1281	1282	1283	1284	1285	1286	1287	1288	1289	1290	1291	1292	1293	1294	1295
51	1296	1297	1298	1299	1300	1301	1302	1303	1304	1305	1306	1307	1308	1309	1310	1311
52	1312	1313	1314	1315	1316	1317	1318	1319	1320	1321	1322	1323	1324	1325	1326	1327
53	1328	1329	1330	1331	1332	1333	1334	1335	1336	1337	1338	1339	1340	1341	1342	1343
54	1344	1345	1346	1347	1348	1349	1350	1351	1352	1353	1354	1355	1356	1357	1358	1359
55	1360	1361	1362	1363	1364	1365	1366	1367	1368	1369	1370	1371	1372	1373	1374	1375
56	1376	1377	1378	1379	1380	1381	1382	1383	1384	1385	1386	1387	1388	1389	1390	1391
57	1392	1393	1394	1395	1396	1397	1398	1399	1400	1401	1402	1403	1404	1405	1406	1407
58	1408	1409	1410	1411	1412	1413	1414	1415	1416	1417	1418	1419	1420	1421	1422	1423
59	1424	1425	1426	1427	1428	1429	1430	1431	1432	1433	1434	1435	1436	1437	1438	1439
5A	1440	1441	1442	1443	1444	1445	1446	1447	1448	1449	1450	1451	1452	1453	1454	1455
5B	1456	1457	1458	1459	1460	1461	1462	1463	1464	1465	1466	1467	1468	1469	1470	1471
5C	1472	1473	1474	1475	1476	1477	1478	1479	1480	1481	1482	1483	1484	1485	1486	1487
5D	1488	1489	1490	1491	1492	1493	1494	1495	1496	1497	1498	1499	1500	1501	1502	1503
5E	1504	1505	1506	1507	1508	1509	1510	1511	1512	1513	1514	1515	1516	1517	1518	1519
5F	1520	1521	1522	1523	1524	1525	1526	1527	1528	1529	1530	1531	1532	1533	1534	1535

HEXADECIMAL–DECIMAL NUMBER CONVERSION TABLE

	0	1	2	3	4	5	6	7	8	9	A	B	C	D	E	F
60	1536	1537	1538	1539	1540	1541	1542	1543	1544	1545	1546	1547	1548	1549	1550	1551
61	1552	1553	1554	1555	1556	1557	1558	1559	1560	1561	1562	1563	1564	1565	1566	1567
62	1568	1569	1570	1571	1572	1573	1574	1575	1576	1577	1578	1579	1580	1581	1582	1583
63	1584	1585	1586	1587	1588	1589	1590	1591	1592	1593	1594	1595	1596	1597	1598	1599
64	1600	1601	1602	1603	1604	1605	1606	1607	1608	1609	1610	1611	1612	1613	1614	1615
65	1616	1617	1618	1619	1620	1621	1622	1623	1624	1625	1626	1627	1628	1629	1630	1631
66	1632	1633	1634	1635	1636	1637	1638	1639	1640	1641	1642	1643	1644	1645	1646	1647
67	1648	1649	1650	1651	1652	1653	1654	1655	1656	1657	1658	1659	1660	1661	1662	1663
68	1664	1665	1666	1667	1668	1669	1670	1671	1672	1673	1674	1675	1676	1677	1678	1679
69	1680	1681	1682	1683	1684	1685	1686	1687	1688	1689	1690	1691	1692	1693	1694	1695
6A	1696	1697	1698	1699	1700	1701	1702	1703	1704	1705	1706	1707	1708	1709	1710	1711
6B	1712	1713	1714	1715	1716	1717	1718	1719	1720	1721	1722	1723	1724	1725	1726	1727
6C	1728	1729	1730	1731	1732	1733	1734	1735	1736	1737	1738	1739	1740	1741	1742	1743
6D	1744	1745	1746	1747	1748	1749	1750	1751	1752	1753	1754	1755	1756	1757	1758	1759
6E	1760	1761	1762	1763	1764	1765	1766	1767	1768	1769	1770	1771	1772	1773	1774	1775
6F	1776	1777	1778	1779	1780	1781	1782	1783	1784	1785	1786	1787	1788	1789	1790	1791
70	1792	1793	1794	1795	1796	1797	1798	1799	1800	1801	1802	1803	1804	1805	1806	1807
71	1808	1809	1810	1811	1812	1813	1814	1815	1816	1817	1818	1819	1820	1821	1822	1823
72	1824	1825	1826	1827	1828	1829	1830	1831	1832	1833	1834	1835	1836	1837	1838	1839
73	1840	1841	1842	1843	1844	1845	1846	1847	1848	1849	1850	1851	1852	1853	1854	1855
74	1856	1857	1858	1859	1860	1861	1862	1863	1864	1865	1866	1867	1868	1869	1870	1871
75	1872	1873	1874	1875	1876	1877	1878	1879	1880	1881	1882	1883	1884	1885	1886	1887
76	1888	1889	1890	1891	1892	1893	1894	1895	1896	1897	1898	1899	1900	1901	1902	1903
77	1904	1905	1906	1907	1908	1909	1910	1911	1912	1913	1914	1915	1916	1917	1918	1919
78	1920	1921	1922	1923	1924	1925	1926	1927	1928	1929	1930	1931	1932	1933	1934	1935
79	1936	1937	1938	1939	1940	1941	1942	1943	1944	1945	1946	1947	1948	1949	1950	1951
7A	1952	1953	1954	1955	1956	1957	1958	1959	1960	1961	1962	1963	1964	1965	1966	1967
7B	1968	1969	1970	1971	1972	1973	1974	1975	1976	1977	1978	1979	1980	1981	1982	1983
7C	1984	1985	1986	1987	1988	1989	1990	1991	1992	1993	1994	1995	1996	1997	1998	1999
7D	2000	2001	2002	2003	2004	2005	2006	2007	2008	2009	2010	2011	2012	2013	2014	2015
7E	2016	2017	2018	2019	2020	2021	2022	2023	2024	2025	2026	2027	2028	2029	2030	2031
7F	2032	2033	2034	2035	2036	2037	2038	2039	2040	2041	2042	2043	2044	2045	2046	2047

HEXADECIMAL–DECIMAL NUMBER CONVERSION TABLE

	0	1	2	3	4	5	6	7	8	9	A	B	C	D	E	F
80	2048	2049	2050	2051	2052	2053	2054	2055	2056	2057	2058	2059	2060	2061	2062	2063
81	2064	2065	2066	2067	2068	2069	2070	2071	2072	2073	2074	2075	2076	2077	2078	2079
82	2080	2081	2082	2083	2084	2085	2086	2087	2088	2089	2090	2091	2092	2093	2094	2095
83	2096	2097	2098	2099	2100	2101	2102	2103	2104	2105	2106	2107	2108	2109	2110	2111
84	2112	2113	2114	2115	2116	2117	2118	2119	2120	2121	2122	2123	2124	2125	2126	2127
85	2128	2129	2130	2131	2132	2133	2134	2135	2136	2137	2138	2139	2140	2141	2142	2143
86	2144	2145	2146	2147	2148	2149	2150	2151	2152	2153	2154	2155	2156	2157	2158	2159
87	2160	2161	2162	2163	2164	2165	2166	2167	2168	2169	2170	2171	2172	2173	2174	2175
88	2176	2177	2178	2179	2180	2181	2182	2183	2184	2185	2186	2187	2188	2189	2190	2191
89	2192	2193	2194	2195	2196	2197	2198	2199	2200	2201	2202	2203	2204	2205	2206	2207
8A	2208	2209	2210	2211	2212	2213	2214	2215	2216	2217	2218	2219	2220	2221	2222	2223
8B	2224	2225	2226	2227	2228	2229	2230	2231	2232	2233	2234	2235	2236	2237	2238	2239
8C	2240	2241	2242	2243	2244	2245	2246	2247	2248	2249	2250	2251	2252	2253	2254	2255
8D	2256	2257	2258	2259	2260	2261	2262	2263	2264	2265	2266	2267	2268	2269	2270	2271
8E	2272	2273	2274	2275	2276	2277	2278	2279	2280	2281	2282	2283	2284	2285	2286	2287
8F	2288	2289	2290	2291	2292	2293	2294	2295	2296	2297	2298	2299	2300	2301	2302	2303
90	2304	2305	2306	2307	2308	2309	2310	2311	2312	2313	2314	2315	2316	2317	2318	2319
91	2320	2321	2322	2323	2324	2325	2326	2327	2328	2329	2330	2331	2332	2333	2334	2335
92	2336	2337	2338	2339	2340	2341	2342	2343	2344	2345	2346	2347	2348	2349	2350	2351
93	2352	2353	2354	2355	2356	2357	2358	2359	2360	2361	2362	2363	2364	2365	2366	2367
94	2368	2369	2370	2371	2372	2373	2374	2375	2376	2377	2378	2379	2380	2381	2382	2383
95	2384	2385	2386	2387	2388	2389	2390	2391	2392	2393	2394	2395	2396	2397	2398	2399
96	2400	2401	2402	2403	2404	2405	2406	2407	2408	2409	2410	2411	2412	2413	2414	2415
97	2416	2417	2418	2419	2420	2421	2422	2423	2424	2425	2426	2427	2428	2429	2430	2431
98	2432	2433	2434	2435	2436	2437	2438	2439	2440	2441	2442	2443	2444	2445	2446	2447
99	2448	2449	2450	2451	2452	2453	2454	2455	2456	2457	2458	2459	2460	2461	2462	2463
9A	2464	2465	2466	2467	2468	2469	2470	2471	2472	2473	2474	2475	2476	2477	2478	2479
9B	2480	2481	2482	2483	2484	2485	2486	2487	2488	2489	2490	2491	2492	2493	2494	2495
9C	2496	2497	2498	2499	2500	2501	2502	2503	2504	2505	2506	2507	2508	2509	2510	2511
9D	2512	2513	2514	2515	2516	2517	2518	2519	2520	2521	2522	2523	2524	2525	2526	2527
9E	2528	2529	2530	2531	2532	2533	2534	2535	2536	2537	2538	2539	2540	2541	2542	2543
9F	2544	2545	2546	2547	2548	2549	2550	2551	2552	2553	2554	2555	2556	2557	2558	2559

HEXADECIMAL-DECIMAL NUMBER CONVERSION TABLE

	0	1	2	3	4	5	6	7	8	9	A	B	C	D	E	F
A0	2560	2561	2562	2563	2564	2565	2566	2567	2568	2569	2570	2571	2572	2573	2574	2575
A1	2576	2577	2578	2579	2580	2581	2582	2583	2584	2585	2586	2587	2588	2589	2590	2591
A2	2592	2593	2594	2595	2596	2597	2598	2599	2600	2601	2602	2603	2604	2605	2606	2607
A3	2608	2609	2610	2611	2612	2613	2614	2615	2616	2617	2618	2619	2620	2621	2622	2623
A4	2624	2625	2626	2627	2628	2629	2630	2631	2632	2633	2634	2635	2636	2637	2638	2639
A5	2640	2641	2642	2643	2644	2645	2646	2647	2648	2649	2650	2651	2652	2653	2654	2655
A6	2656	2657	2658	2659	2660	2661	2662	2663	2664	2665	2666	2667	2668	2669	2670	2671
A7	2672	2673	2674	2675	2676	2677	2678	2679	2680	2681	2682	2683	2684	2685	2686	2687
A8	2688	2689	2690	2691	2692	2693	2694	2695	2696	2697	2698	2699	2700	2701	2702	2703
A9	2704	2705	2706	2707	2708	2709	2710	2711	2712	2713	2714	2715	2716	2717	2718	2719
AA	2720	2721	2722	2723	2724	2725	2726	2727	2728	2729	2730	2731	2732	2733	2734	2735
AB	2736	2737	2738	2739	2740	2741	2742	2743	2744	2745	2746	2747	2748	2749	2750	2751
AC	2752	2753	2754	2755	2756	2757	2758	2759	2760	2761	2762	2763	2764	2765	2766	2767
AD	2768	2769	2770	2771	2772	2773	2774	2775	2776	2777	2778	2779	2780	2781	2782	2783
AE	2784	2785	2786	2787	2788	2789	2790	2791	2792	2793	2794	2795	2796	2797	2798	2799
AF	2800	2801	2802	2803	2804	2805	2806	2807	2808	2809	2810	2811	2812	2813	2814	2815
B0	2816	2817	2818	2819	2820	2821	2822	2823	2824	2825	2826	2827	2828	2829	2830	2831
B1	2832	2833	2834	2835	2836	2837	2838	2839	2840	2841	2842	2843	2844	2845	2846	2847
B2	2848	2849	2850	2851	2852	2853	2854	2855	2856	2857	2858	2859	2860	2861	2862	2863
B3	2864	2865	2866	2867	2868	2869	2870	2871	2872	2873	2874	2875	2876	2877	2878	2879
B4	2880	2881	2882	2883	2884	2885	2886	2887	2888	2889	2890	2891	2892	2893	2894	2895
B5	2896	2897	2898	2899	2900	2901	2902	2903	2904	2905	2906	2907	2908	2909	2910	2911
B6	2912	2913	2914	2915	2916	2917	2918	2919	2920	2921	2922	2923	2924	2925	2926	2927
B7	2928	2929	2930	2931	2932	2933	2934	2935	2936	2937	2938	2939	2940	2941	2942	2943
B8	2944	2945	2946	2947	2948	2949	2950	2951	2952	2953	2954	2955	2956	2957	2958	2959
B9	2960	2961	2962	2963	2964	2965	2966	2967	2968	2969	2970	2971	2972	2973	2974	2975
BA	2976	2977	2978	2979	2980	2981	2982	2983	2984	2985	2986	2987	2988	2989	2990	2991
BB	2992	2993	2994	2995	2996	2997	2998	2999	3000	3001	3002	3003	3004	3005	3006	3007
BC	3008	3009	3010	3011	3012	3013	3014	3015	3016	3017	3018	3019	3020	3021	3022	3023
BD	3024	3025	3026	3027	3028	3029	3030	3031	3032	3033	3034	3035	3036	3037	3038	3039
BE	3040	3041	3042	3043	3044	3045	3046	3047	3048	3049	3050	3051	3052	3053	3054	3055
BF	3056	3057	3058	3059	3060	3061	3062	3063	3064	3065	3066	3067	3068	3069	3070	3071

HEXADECIMAL-DECIMAL NUMBER CONVERSION TABLE

	0	1	2	3	4	5	6	7	8	9	A	B	C	D	E	F
C0	3072	3073	3074	3075	3076	3077	3078	3079	3080	3081	3082	3083	3084	3085	3086	3087
C1	3088	3089	3090	3091	3092	3093	3094	3095	3096	3097	3098	3099	3100	3101	3102	3103
C2	3104	3105	3106	3107	3108	3109	3110	3111	3112	3113	3114	3115	3116	3117	3118	3119
C3	3120	3121	3122	3123	3124	3125	3126	3127	3128	3129	3130	3131	3132	3133	3134	3135
C4	3136	3137	3138	3139	3140	3141	3142	3143	3144	3145	3146	3147	3148	3149	3150	3151
C5	3152	3153	3154	3155	3156	3157	3158	3159	3160	3161	3162	3163	3164	3165	3166	3167
C6	3168	3169	3170	3171	3172	3173	3174	3175	3176	3177	3178	3179	3180	3181	3182	3183
C7	3184	3185	3186	3187	3188	3189	3190	3191	3192	3193	3194	3195	3196	3197	3198	3199
C8	3200	3201	3202	3203	3204	3205	3206	3207	3208	3209	3210	3211	3212	3213	3214	3215
C9	3216	3217	3218	3219	3220	3221	3222	3223	3224	3225	3226	3227	3228	3229	3230	3231
CA	3232	3233	3234	3235	3236	3237	3238	3239	3240	3241	3242	3243	3244	3245	3246	3247
CB	3248	3249	3250	3251	3252	3253	3254	3255	3256	3257	3258	3259	3260	3261	3262	3263
CC	3264	3265	3266	3267	3268	3269	3270	3271	3272	3273	3274	3275	3276	3277	3278	3279
CD	3280	3281	3282	3283	3284	3285	3286	3287	3288	3289	3290	3291	3292	3293	3294	3295
CE	3296	3297	3298	3299	3300	3301	3302	3303	3304	3305	3306	3307	3308	3309	3310	3311
CF	3312	3313	3314	3315	3316	3317	3318	3319	3320	3321	3322	3323	3324	3325	3326	3327
D0	3328	3329	3330	3331	3332	3333	3334	3335	3336	3337	3338	3339	3340	3341	3342	3343
D1	3344	3345	3346	3347	3348	3349	3350	3351	3352	3353	3354	3355	3356	3357	3358	3359
D2	3360	3361	3362	3363	3364	3365	3366	3367	3368	3369	3370	3371	3372	3373	3374	3375
D3	3376	3377	3378	3379	3380	3381	3382	3383	3384	3385	3386	3387	3388	3389	3390	3391
D4	3392	3393	3394	3395	3396	3397	3398	3399	3400	3401	3402	3403	3404	3405	3406	3407
D5	3408	3409	3410	3411	3412	3413	3414	3415	3416	3417	3418	3419	3420	3421	3422	3423
D6	3424	3425	3426	3427	3428	3429	3430	3431	3432	3433	3434	3435	3436	3437	3438	3439
D7	3440	3441	3442	3443	3444	3445	3446	3447	3448	3449	3450	3451	3452	3453	3454	3455
D8	3456	3457	3458	3459	3460	3461	3462	3463	3464	3465	3466	3467	3468	3469	3470	3471
D9	3472	3473	3474	3475	3476	3477	3478	3479	3480	3481	3482	3483	3484	3485	3486	3487
DA	3488	3489	3490	3491	3492	3493	3494	3495	3496	3497	3498	3499	3500	3501	3502	3503
DB	3504	3505	3506	3507	3508	3509	3510	3511	3512	3513	3514	3515	3516	3517	3518	3519
DC	3520	3521	3522	3523	3524	3525	3526	3527	3528	3529	3530	3531	3532	3533	3534	3535
DD	3536	3537	3538	3539	3540	3541	3542	3543	3544	3545	3546	3547	3548	3549	3550	3551
DE	3552	3553	3554	3555	3556	3557	3558	3559	3560	3561	3562	3563	3564	3565	3566	3567
DF	3568	3569	3570	3571	3572	3573	3574	3575	3576	3577	3578	3579	3580	3581	3582	3583

HEXADECIMAL-DECIMAL NUMBER CONVERSION TABLE

	0	1	2	3	4	5	6	7	8	9	A	B	C	D	E	F
E0	3584	3585	3586	3587	3588	3589	3590	3591	3592	3593	3594	3595	3596	3597	3598	3599
E1	3600	3601	3602	3603	3604	3605	3606	3607	3608	3609	3610	3611	3612	3613	3614	3615
E2	3616	3617	3618	3619	3620	3621	3622	3623	3624	3625	3626	3627	3628	3629	3630	3631
E3	3632	3633	3634	3635	3636	3637	3638	3639	3640	3641	3642	3643	3644	3645	3646	3647
E4	3648	3649	3650	3651	3652	3653	3654	3655	3656	3657	3658	3659	3660	3661	3662	3663
E5	3664	3665	3666	3667	3668	3669	3670	3671	3672	3673	3674	3675	3676	3677	3678	3679
E6	3680	3681	3682	3683	3684	3685	3686	3687	3688	3689	3690	3691	3692	3693	3694	3695
E7	3696	3697	3698	3699	3700	3701	3702	3703	3704	3705	3706	3707	3708	3709	3710	3711
E8	3712	3713	3714	3715	3716	3717	3718	3719	3720	3721	3722	3723	3724	3725	3726	3727
E9	3728	3729	3730	3731	3732	3733	3734	3735	3736	3737	3738	3739	3740	3741	3742	3743
EA	3744	3745	3746	3747	3748	3749	3750	3751	3752	3753	3754	3755	3756	3757	3758	3759
EB	3760	3761	3762	3763	3764	3765	3766	3767	3768	3769	3770	3771	3772	3773	3774	3775
EC	3776	3777	3778	3779	3780	3781	3782	3783	3784	3785	3786	3787	3788	3789	3790	3791
ED	3792	3793	3794	3795	3796	3797	3798	3799	3800	3801	3802	3803	3804	3805	3806	3807
EE	3808	3809	3810	3811	3812	3813	3814	3815	3816	3817	3818	3819	3820	3821	3822	3823
EF	3824	3825	3826	3827	3828	3829	3830	3831	3832	3833	3834	3835	3836	3837	3838	3839
F0	3840	3841	3842	3843	3844	3845	3846	3847	3848	3849	3850	3851	3852	3853	3854	3855
F1	3856	3857	3858	3859	3860	3861	3862	3863	3864	3865	3866	3867	3868	3869	3870	3871
F2	3872	3873	3874	3875	3876	3877	3878	3879	3880	3881	3882	3883	3884	3885	3886	3887
F3	3888	3889	3890	3891	3892	3893	3894	3895	3896	3897	3898	3899	3900	3901	3902	3903
F4	3904	3905	3906	3907	3908	3909	3910	3911	3912	3913	3914	3915	3916	3917	3918	3919
F5	3920	3921	3922	3923	3924	3925	3926	3927	3928	3929	3930	3931	3932	3933	3934	3935
F6	3936	3937	3938	3939	3940	3941	3942	3943	3944	3945	3946	3947	3948	3949	3950	3951
F7	3952	3953	3954	3955	3956	3957	3958	3959	3960	3961	3962	3963	3964	3965	3966	3967
F8	3968	3969	3970	3971	3972	3973	3974	3975	3976	3977	3978	3979	3980	3981	3982	3983
F9	3984	3985	3986	3987	3988	3989	3990	3991	3992	3993	3994	3995	3996	3997	3998	3999
FA	4000	4001	4002	4003	4004	4005	4006	4007	4008	4009	4010	4011	4012	4013	4014	4015
FB	4016	4017	4018	4019	4020	4021	4022	4023	4024	4025	4026	4027	4028	4029	4030	4031
FC	4032	4033	4034	4035	4036	4037	4038	4039	4040	4041	4042	4043	4044	4045	4046	4047
FD	4048	4049	4050	4051	4052	4053	4054	4055	4056	4057	4058	4059	4060	4061	4062	4063
FE	4064	4065	4066	4067	4068	4069	4070	4071	4072	4073	4074	4075	4076	4077	4078	4079
FF	4080	4081	4082	4083	4084	4085	4086	4087	4088	4089	4090	4091	4092	4093	4094	4095